The Wonderful World
of New Jersey

The Wonderful World

New Brunswick, New Jersey, 1955

VICTOR L. CROWELL, Ed.D.

# of NEW JERSEY

Our Natural Resources

RUTGERS UNIVERSITY PRESS

Foreword

For many years, this book has been badly needed in New Jersey. There has been a serious dearth of suitable printed material on the elementary level to help pupils and other interested citizens to answer their questions, solve their problems, and acquire understanding about the natural resources of this state and the need for conserving them.

This book is worth waiting for. Pupils, teachers, and the lay public will find it stimulating, challenging, and authoritative. It contains much important information not heretofore easily procurable. The generous use of photographs and diagrams will make it useful and interesting to children as well as adults. The care with which reading difficulties have been minimized should make it possible for pupils as far down as the fourth or fifth grade to use it for reference purposes.

The author is especially well qualified. He has developed the material in the book in a long span of teaching conservation to students in teachers colleges and teachers in service. Conservation of New Jersey's resources has been a hobby of his. It may safely be stated that writing this book has been a "labor of love" as well as a real service to our schools.

I feel sure that the book will be widely used at various levels for various purposes in schools, libraries, and homes. It will help make many people more effective citizens of New Jersey.

THOMAS J. DURELL
*Formerly Assistant Commissioner of Education
in charge of Elementary Education*

v

Preface

New Jersey is a rapidly growing state. This rapid growth makes it essential that the people of the state know about the natural resources of New Jersey and about the many problems related to their management and control. It is particularly important that the boys and girls who are now in school be given an opportunity to learn about our natural resources. They are the ones who will soon be helping to make decisions concerning their wise use, and they are the ones who will suffer if these resources are neglected. Without enlightened citizens, our resources may soon be in a very critical condition. Many are already inadequate for our needs.

It is hoped that this book will introduce to many boys and girls, as well as to adult readers, aspects of our state with which they are now unfamiliar. There is no other single volume to which students, teachers, or laymen can refer to find out about the natural resources of our state. Although this book was written primarily for use in the schools of New Jersey, it is the hope of the author that it may fill a long-felt need, expressed by many adults, for an authoritative source of information about the present status of our resources.

Much of the material in this book has heretofore appeared only in technical reports, which the layman has had difficulty in reading. The author has for many years been privileged to associate with leaders in the field of conservation in New Jersey. He has drawn freely from the knowledge gained through association with these persons and is greatly indebted to them.

The author has attempted to take a subject which has large social significance and to present it in such a manner as to represent a fusion or integration of the natural sciences and the social studies. It is hoped that teachers of both the natural sciences and the social studies will find this volume helpful to them. It might well serve as a textbook in the upper grades and as a reference for teachers of the lower grades, who will wish to adapt parts of it for units suitable to their grade level. No teacher, at any grade level, who is trying to teach effectively, can ignore his responsibility for teaching about the natural resources of New Jersey and the United States. Other writers have written about the broad problems of the conservation of natural resources for the United States as a whole. For that reason, this volume is restricted to a consideration of the resources of New Jersey.

Acknowledgments

The author wishes to acknowledge his indebtedness to the many persons who have given freely of their time and experience in reading critically the manuscript of this book and in discussing the contents with him. Each chapter has been read by one or more specialists in the subject treated in that chapter. Each chapter has also been read critically by two or more experienced teachers. All these people have made many helpful suggestions.

Every effort has been made to present accurate, authoritative information, but if any errors do occur, the author accepts full responsibility. The author is especially grateful to the following persons for their careful reading of the manuscript, either in part or in its entirety, and for their constructive suggestions and criticisms:

Mr. Charles Harp, Professor of Science, State Teachers College at Trenton.

Miss Mabel Harp, Elementary School Teacher.

Dr. Meredith E. Johnson, State Geologist, State Department of Conservation and Economic Development, Trenton.

Mr. E. B. Moore, Chief of Forestry Cooperation Section, State Department of Conservation and Economic Development, Trenton.

Dr. Thurlow Nelson, Professor of Zoology, Rutgers University, New Brunswick.

Mrs. Isabelle Riddel, Elementary School Teacher.

ACKNOWLEDGMENTS

Dr. Miriam Sachs, Chief of Bureau on Adult and Occupational Health, State Department of Health, Trenton.

Mr. William J. Seidel, State Fire Warden, State Department of Conservation and Economic Development, Trenton.

Mr. George R. Shanklin, Assistant Director, Division of Water Policy and Supply, State Department of Conservation and Economic Development, Trenton.

Dr. Lois M. Shoemaker, Professor of Science, State Teachers College at Trenton.

Mr. Harry Slayback, Extension Soil Conservationist, Rutgers University, New Brunswick.

Grateful acknowledgment is made to Dr. Thomas J. Durell, former Assistant Commissioner of Education, State Department of Education, Trenton, for his help and encouragement in initiating work on the manuscript.

Many persons have given whole-heartedly of their time in providing photographs for use in this book. The sources of the photographs used in this work are given with the pictures except in the case of that on the title page, which was supplied by Mr. John Cunningham, author of *This Is New Jersey*. The author is particularly appreciative of the assistance rendered by his colleague, Miss Anne Voss, in preparing the diagrams and drawings.

Contents

CONTENTS

The Wonderful World
of New Jersey

Chapter One

This State of Ours

Introduction

New Jersey is a fine state in which to live. Over five million people live and work in New Jersey. Most of these people have good jobs and comfortable homes and are happy to live in our state. On weekends and during vacation periods they can easily and quickly go to the seashore, the woods, or the mountains. Thousands of other people from all over the country come to New Jersey to enjoy our resorts. New Jersey is such a fine state in which to work and live because it is rich in natural resources. Without the many natural resources which we have in New Jersey, our way of living would be very different from what it now is.

Perhaps some of you may wonder what is meant by the term "natural resources." By this is meant any things which occur naturally and which are of benefit or value to human beings. I am sure that all of you could prepare a list of things which would fit this definition. Many of the items would probably be similar to those included in this book. Perhaps you would include on your list our beaches, lakes, and forests. Some might mention water and wildlife. That would be correct. These are all examples of natural resources. As you read this book you will find that there are many natural resources about which all of us should know.

Unless we use wisely all of the resources which we have,

3

our state cannot continue to grow and prosper. If our state is not prosperous, the people who live in it will not prosper. They will not be able to live as well as most of them now live. It is, therefore, the duty of every citizen to learn about the natural resources of his state. He must constantly be thinking of the best ways of using them. Nothing is more important to any of us.

Some of the problems relating to the wise use of our natural resources are very large problems. You may not be able to do much about solving some of them until you are older and can vote. These problems will require much thought. Some will require wise legislation before they are finally solved. However, in almost every case, there are many things that you and I can do, right now, to use these natural resources to the advantage of all. We may already be doing some of these things. Perhaps you can make a list of the things you are already doing to make wise use of our natural resources. You will notice that the word "use" appeared in the last sentence. Many persons think that conservation of natural resources means only to save and not use. The definition given by the former President, Theodore Roosevelt, who was a great conservationist, is a good one. He said, "Conservation means development as much as it does protection." Unless we use wisely and develop what we have, we are not being good conservationists.

Each chapter of this book is going to tell us something about one or more of the natural resources of New Jersey. We will be better able to appreciate and understand these chapters if we first learn a little about the geography of our state. It will help us also, if we learn a little about our population and how the people earn their living. The remainder of this chapter will tell us some interesting facts about New

Jersey. These will often be referred to in the chapters which follow.

The Geography of New Jersey

New Jersey is a very small state. The total area is only 8,204 square miles. There are forty-four states in the United States which are larger than New Jersey. Its greatest length is 166 miles from High Point to Cape May. At its narrowest point, it is only 32 miles from Trenton to Raritan Bay.

If you were to take a trip from one end of the state to the other, you would find that New Jersey is composed of two quite different parts. Lay a ruler on a map of New Jersey so that one edge of the ruler touches both Trenton and Carteret. You will now have divided the state into two parts. Each of these sections is very different from the other in many ways. The northern section is called the Appalachian Province. The southern section is called the Coastal Plain.

The Appalachian Province includes about two fifths of the state. Scientists often divide it still further into three divisions or zones. Each zone differs from the others, just as the Appalachian Province differs from the Coastal Plain. The zones of the Appalachian Province will be described briefly, because they will be referred to in other chapters.

The zone that is farthest to the northwest is called the Appalachian Valley. The Valley extends south of New Jersey into other states. In New Jersey, it is a broad belt of valleys and ridges. The principal valley in New Jersey is the Kittatinny Valley. In New Jersey, this valley is 12 miles wide and 40 miles long. It is separated from the Delaware Valley by a ridge known as Kittatinny Mountain. This is a very beautiful section. In this zone is the highest point of land in the state. There is a State Park at this point, and it has been appropriately called High Point State Park. At the base of

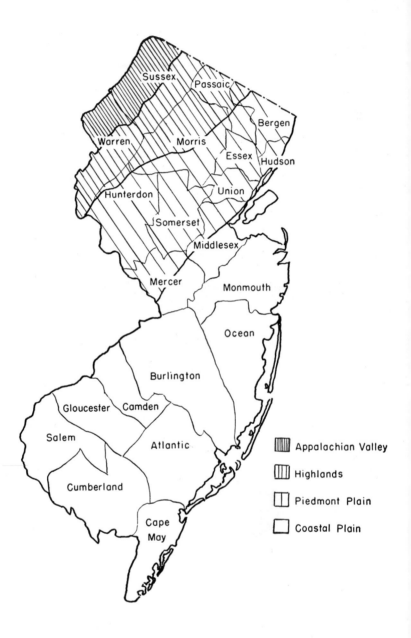

Sussex

Passaic

Bergen

Warren

Morris

Essex

Hudson

Hunterdon

Union

Somerset

Middlesex

Mercer

Monmouth

Ocean

Burlington

Gloucester

Camden

Salem

Atlantic

Cumberland

Cape
May

Appalachian Valley

Highlands

Piedmont Plain

Coastal Plain

a monument in this park, the height above sea level is 1,804 feet.

Southeast of the Appalachian Valley zone is a section which in New Jersey is called the Highlands. In other parts

N. J. Dept. of Conservation
and Economic Development

High Point Tower across Lake Marcia

of the United States, this zone is called the Appalachian Mountain zone. Farther to the south in the United States, there are high mountains in this zone. Here there are a great many kinds of interesting rocks and minerals, about which we shall learn more later. There are many hills and valleys in this section, also.

Nearer to the central part of the state, there is a third zone. It is called the Piedmont Plain. The word Piedmont comes from two French words which mean foot and mountain.

Piedmont is a good name for the zone because it lies at the foot of the Highlands or Appalachian Mountain zone. The land of the Piedmont is more level than the rest of the land in the Appalachian Province. There are some hills in this

N. J. Dept. of Conservation
and Economic Development

Normanock Brook in Stokes State Forest. Streams like this are very important resources, which must be conserved.

section, about which we shall learn more in the chapter entitled "Our Buried Treasures." The Piedmont Plain is the section in which the greatest number of people live. More people live here than in all of the other sections combined.

The southern section of the state, which lies below the line drawn from Trenton to Carteret, is called the Coastal Plain. It extends over three fifths of the state. Here the earth is very flat, and not very far above sea level. The highest part of the Coastal Plain is only 400 feet above the ocean. This is in

Monmouth County. Another difference between the Coastal Plain and the Appalachian Province is in the type of rocks found in each. On the Coastal Plain, there are very few solid rocks. Most of the Coastal Plain contains sand and clay which have not become very solid or hard. We shall find in other chapters that the types of rock in a region often influence the types of industry found there. Rocks and soils are both natural resources which influence our lives.

Other natural resources which have affected the growth of our state are the rivers and streams. New Jersey has several large rivers either entirely within the state or along its boundaries. In the northern part of the state, there are the Hudson, Passaic, Hackensack, and Raritan Rivers. The Delaware extends along the entire length of the state. In the Coastal Plain section of New Jersey, there are the Mullica, Toms, Maurice, and Great Egg Harbor Rivers.

Population

Although New Jersey is forty-fifth among the states in size, it ranks eighth in population. The 1950 census showed that we had a population of 4,835,329. Since then our population has increased so that now we have over 5,250,000 people living in New Jersey. We shall soon see that having so many people in a small area raises problems about our natural resources. It is hard to have plenty of water for so many people, for example. A large population also requires many State Forests and State Parks for recreation. It is hard to keep enough animals in the woods and streams so that sportsmen can enjoy hunting and fishing.

Occupations

How do all the people in our state earn a living? Our state is rather unusual because, although New Jersey is a highly

9

industrial state, we also have many small farms. In fact, New Jersey is often called "The Garden State." There are about 24,830 farms in New Jersey, and the state ranks first, among

Seabrook Farms Co. Photo

Spinach is one of the many crops which make New Jersey known as "The Garden State." Almost two million bushels are grown here each year.

all of the states, in the farm income per acre of land. In New Jersey, in 1953, the income from one acre was $161.00. The next two highest states in this respect were Delaware and Connecticut. The total income from farm products in New Jersey each year is about $400,000,000. New Jersey is known in other parts of the country for its cranberries, blueberries, and potatoes. Large quantities of our apples are shipped each year to England and to countries in South America.

The state also holds high rank in the dairy and poultry industries. Four New Jersey counties are among the first ten

Standard Oil Co. (N. J.)

A dairy farm in the hills of Sussex County. Without farms like this, our large cities could not exist.

in the entire United States in the value and number of eggs and chickens sold. These counties are Cumberland, Hunterdon, Monmouth, and Ocean Counties. The well-drained soil and moderate climate have made poultry farming a successful business in New Jersey. New Jersey is second in milk production per cow in the United States. In this state, the average for one cow for a year is 3,493 quarts of milk.

New Jersey has several food-processing companies that are

11

known all over the world. Among these are Seabrook Farms
Company, Campbell Soup Company, H. J. Heinz Company,
and P. J. Ritter Company. Plants in southern New Jersey for
canning and freezing foods are among the largest in the
world.

Seabrook Farms Co. Photo

An aerial view of part of Seabrook Farms, showing strip cropping.
Planting crops in strips helps prevent soil erosion.

New Jersey ranks second in the United States in the percentage of farms that have electrical service.

Many of the residents of New Jersey work in our numerous industries. There are over 13,000 different kinds of industries in the state. These cause us to rank sixth in the United
States in the value of manufactured products. We have oil
refining industries, as well as factories for the manufacture of
silk, wool, and rayon products. A great variety of manufac-

turing processes are carried on here. We rank first in the United States in the dollar value of our chemical products.

Most of these many industries were established in New Jersey because of some favorable natural resource. Our farms could not exist, were it not for natural resources. Our cli-

Standard Oil Co. (N. J.)

Silk and rayon mills along the Passaic River, Paterson, New Jersey

mate, our soil types, our closeness to good harbors, and our plentiful water suppply have all contributed to the development of our state.

In the early days of our state's history, many towns were settled where natural resources were available. Water power was once a more important source of power than it now is. Mills were located where water power was available. The waterfalls at Paterson were the reason why that city was established there on the Passaic River. Some other cities that were settled because of water power are Passaic, Bridgeton,

13

Millville, Lambertville, and Boonton. Electrical power was not available then. Today, it can be sent long distances. The glass industry in Cumberland County, in the southern part of the state, is another example of an industry which developed because of a natural resource—the sand in the vicinity. Another is the brick-making industry in Middlesex County, established where clay was found. Many of these same industries are operating today.

Harbors form a natural resource which has stimulated the growth of many communities. Many of our large cities, like Camden and Jersey City, have been helped to grow because they are near good harbors.

Climate

Without a favorable climate, we could not have the farms or the industries we now have. We all live very comfortably because of the favorable climate. By "climate" is meant the weather which we have over a period of many years. Many of us do not think of a good climate as a natural resource.

In New Jersey, we have plenty of sunshine and moderate temperatures. Our sunshine is only about 55 per cent of the possible amount, but it is adequate for our comfort and health. Our annual temperature averages 54 degrees Fahrenheit. In Sussex County, the January temperature averages 27 degrees, and in Cape May County, the average is 35 degrees. The average July temperature in Sussex County is 72 degrees, and in Cape May County, it is 74 degrees. The extremes in New Jersey are 110 and −34 degrees.

Precipitation is a factor of our climate that is very important in determining how our people live and what work they do. Precipitation means forms of water that fall from the sky. Rain, snow, sleet, and hail are common forms of precipitation. Precipitation is measured in terms of inches of water.

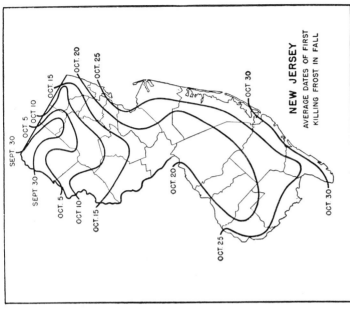

NEW JERSEY

AVERAGE DATES OF FIRST
KILLING FROST IN FALL

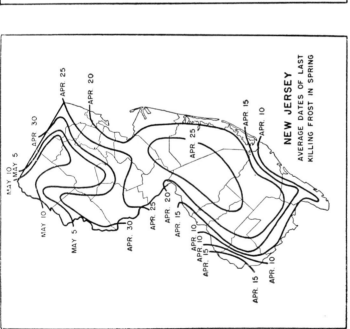

NEW JERSEY

AVERAGE DATES OF LAST
KILLING FROST IN SPRING

U. S. Dept. of Agriculture

Average dates of first killing frost in fall and last killing frost in spring

It takes about ten inches of snow to equal one inch of rain. The average precipitation in New Jersey is almost 46 inches. That means that if all the water which came from rain and snow and other forms of precipitation were left on the ground, we would have water 46 inches deep at the end of a year. Past records show an annual average precipitation of 44.42 inches at Trenton. Our snow is usually not so heavy as to cause great inconvenience. At Trenton, the average amount of snow in one year is 23 inches. Cape May County gets only about 14 inches a year. The northern part of the state averages 50 inches.

One very important factor of climate for farmers and city gardeners is the length of the growing season. If frost comes late in the spring and early in the fall, certain crops cannot be grown. We have a very favorable growing season. It varies with the part of the state in which one lives.

Our Interest in Natural Resources

In the chapters which follow, we shall learn more about the things which nature has given us and which are of great benefit to us. We shall learn about the problems of securing enough good water to enable our many industries and farms to operate. We shall see how important our soil is to us, and how fortunate we are to have many different types of soil. These and many other things will probably be new to you, but are things about which we should all know.

Before long, many of us will be out of school and earning our own living. Some will work in factories. Others will be in business or on a farm. Some will be in professions. Wherever we are, and whatever we do, it will be important to us to see that our state remains prosperous. It can only do so if we conserve our natural resources wisely. The more we can learn about these resources and how to make the best use of them, the better citizens we will be. Without them our ways of life will be changed considerably. Perhaps a couple of illustrations will make this clearer.

For recreation many of us, either now or later, will some day want to go swimming in our lakes or oceans or go fishing in our streams. It would be a great disappointment to find that there were no fish or that we could not swim, because the waters were polluted. If our towns and cities and our factories do not dispose of their wastes properly, our waters will be polluted more than they now are. Many are now not safe to use, and fish cannot live in many streams.

All through life we shall probably enjoy fresh fruits and vegetables. If we allow our soil to be misused, however, we may have to do without these products of our farms and gardens. Also, much money will have to be spent to build up the soil which we waste. As a result, prices will rise, and taxes will increase.

There are many references in the newspapers and on radio and television to our natural resources. It will help you to understand these references better if you learn about the subject now. Also, by talking about natural resources with your parents and friends, you will help them to vote more intelligently. Some day, you also will vote on questions having to do with natural resources.

After you have studied the other chapters in this book, you will understand the importance of conservation of our natural resources. You may want to make the following pledge:

CONSERVATION PLEDGE

I give my pledge as an American to save and faithfully to defend from waste the natural resources of my country—its soil and minerals, its forests, waters, and wildlife.

If everyone lived up to that pledge our state and our country would be finer places in which to live.

SOME THINGS TO THINK ABOUT

1. What natural resources favored the early development of New Jersey?

2. Why are there so few industries in Sussex, Ocean, and Morris Counties and so many in Mercer, Essex, and Middlesex Counties?

3. What natural resources have contributed to the position of leadership in agriculture and industry which New Jersey holds?

4. Why is New Jersey called "The Garden State"?

5. What names other than "Garden State" would be appropriate for New Jersey?

6. Have natural resources of any kind contributed to the development of your county? How?

7. Why was your town settled, or located, where it now is?

8. How has a favorable climate helped our state to develop and prosper?

9. Why should all intelligent citizens of all ages be interested in the natural resources of our state?

SOME THINGS TO DO

1. Make a list of the principal agricultural or industrial products produced in your county.

2. Find out what natural resources have contributed most to your county's development.

3. Draw or trace a map of New Jersey, and locate on it the principal rivers.

4. Find out what three states are smaller in size than New Jersey.

5. Make a list of all the natural resources you can think of.

6. Locate on a map the greatest length of our state and the narrowest width.

7. Locate High Point State Park on a map of New Jersey.

8. Secure from a service station a map of New Jersey, and on it draw lines to show the boundaries of the twenty-one counties.

9. Visit your local food market, and see if you can find out what foods sold there were grown in New Jersey.

10. Take a trip to see one or more of the zones or divisions of the state. Observe the scenery, and compare it with that where you live.

SOME TERMS YOU NEED TO KNOW

Appalachian Province—The name given to a belt or zone of mountains, extending from New York to Alabama. In New Jersey, the northern two fifths of the state are included in it. The boundary between the Coastal Plain and the Appalachian Province runs on nearly a straight line between New Brunswick and Trenton.

Climate—The average condition of the weather over a period of many years.

Coastal Plain—The name given to the flat or gently rolling land which borders a coast. The southern three fifths of New Jersey are a part of the Atlantic Coastal Plain. The Atlantic Coastal Plain extends from northern New Jersey to Florida. It is from 50 to 100 miles wide.

Conservation—The wise use and planned management of natural resources.

Natural resources—Anything which occurs naturally and is of benefit or value to man.

Precipitation—Something which falls from the sky, like rain or snow.

19

Chapter Two

Water—The Lifeblood of New Jersey

Section 1. HOW WE USE WATER

Perhaps you are wondering why this chapter is entitled
"Water—The Lifeblood of New Jersey." Blood is necessary
for life. If we lose much blood we die. Without water, our
communities and our state would die. Water is as necessary
to New Jersey as blood is to each living being.

Did you ever stop to think how necessary water is to you
and to your community? Water is one of the three basic
needs of all life. Air and food are the other two basic needs.
Most of us take water for granted, just as we do the air
around us. We should not do this. In general, the people of
New Jersey have been very fortunate so far. Most of us have
had all of the water that we needed in our homes and in our
communities. In some areas of New Jersey, people have not
been so fortunate. The newspapers often report on local
water shortages. Such shortages of water are usually the result of failure to develop properly the water resources that
are available. A long drought would seriously affect every
citizen in our state. This is not because we lack water, but
because we lack storage facilities. If it is to grow, our state
needs new reservoirs. Some people do not realize that we
must have more reservoirs to store water for our many needs.

Water in Plants and Animals

All living things are made up of cells. In the human brain alone, there are about thirteen billion cells. We all know that water is necessary to build new cells in plants and animals. Did you know, too, that the body of the average man contains twelve gallons of water? About seven tenths of the weight of the body is made up of water. A hundred-pound boy has almost seventy pounds of water in his body. This water comes from what we eat and drink. Our blood, our bones, and our muscles all contain water. Each of us should take in at least three pints of water each day. Some of this may be included in the foods which we eat or drink. More water would probably be better for us. A man can go without food for several weeks, but he will die if he goes without water for more than several days. All animals need water, just as we do.

Plants also need water for their cells. You all have seen what happens to a plant which does not receive water. It withers and dies. Of course, some plants, like the cacti, which live in deserts, can get along with less water than others. In order to produce one pound of corn, about 750 quarts of water are used by the corn plants. Four hundred quarts of water are required to produce one pound of wheat.

Plants get their food materials from the soil. The minerals in the soil are dissolved in water. The water and the dissolved minerals enter the plant through small root hairs and go up to the leaves through the stem. In the leaves, food is manufactured by the combining of water with carbon dioxide and minerals. The extra water evaporates from the leaves into the air. Scientists call this evaporation of water from plants by a special name. It is called transpiration. A single tree may give off by transpiration as much as 125 gallons of water a day.

It is to keep up this steady flow that so much water is needed by plants.

Water for Cleaning

Think how dirty we and our homes would be if we did not have water! We could not have our modern bathrooms if we did not have large quantities of water. If you take a shower bath you probably use about 25 gallons of water. A tub bath requires about 35 gallons of water. Each time the toilet is flushed, from six to eight gallons of water are used. Think of all of the water used to wash dishes and to do the laundry at home. In the cities, water is often used to wash off the streets. On the farms, water is used to clean milking machines, pails, and other equipment. Sometimes barns are washed out with water. Whether we live in the city or in the country, we need large quantities of water. This water must be clean and pure.

Water in Industry

Great quantities of water are used in manufacturing foods, clothing, and other necessary things. To make one pound of rayon about 100 gallons of water are used. It takes about 500 gallons of water to manufacture one yard of wool cloth. Near Princeton, in Mercer County, is a factory where penicillin is made. This one factory uses over 100,000 gallons of water every day.

Many factories produce waste material which would, if discharged into streams, pollute the water. This pollution might kill fish and other forms of wildlife. Often the waste materials have odors which are objectionable. To prevent this pollution, factories use large quantities of water to dilute the industrial wastes.

Many industries use a considerable amount of water in

their boilers to generate power. Factories also use it as a cooling agent in the manufacture of steel and plastics. One hundred thousand gallons of water are used to produce one ton of steel. Much water is used in the refining of oil and other related products. In the Raritan Valley, over 100 million gallons of water are used by chemical concerns each day.

If it were not for an abundant supply of water, many industries would not have been located in New Jersey. These illustrations are just a few of the many which might have been given to show how water is used in industry. Perhaps there are industries in your county which use water. Do you know of any?

Water and Air Conditioning

Today when we go into a large store, office building, or theater, we expect it to be air-conditioned. In our homes, we do not ordinarily use water for air conditioning if we have a small unit. For air conditioning large buildings, it is cheaper to use water to remove the heat from the air. This can be done only if water is available, of course. A single department store, in one of our large cities, uses about two million gallons a day for air conditioning. This is enough water to fill a good-size lake or pond. A standard-size swimming pool holds only about 75,000 gallons. Some communities have not made provisions for collecting and storing water in large enough quantities. Other communities lack facilities to distribute water to the people. Using too much water for air conditioning tends to create shortages in parts of the state where facilities are inadequate.

Water and Wildlife

Without pure, fresh water, our wildlife cannot live. When streams dry up, the wildlife in them may die. Even if the stream is only partly dried up, the fish may die or have to leave the stream. In shallow streams the water is heated by the sun, and some fish cannot live in warm water. Trout, for example, must have cool water.

North Jersey District
Water Supply Commission

West Brook, one of the main feeders of the Wanaque Reservoir

When streams become polluted, the animal life may also die or leave the stream. In highly polluted streams, the oxygen, which all animals need, is used up by combining with the chemicals and waste materials that cause pollution. Without plenty of oxygen in the water, fish and other animals soon die.

Oysters are grown in large numbers in New Jersey. Oysters live in salt water which has been diluted by fresh-water streams. If our streams are polluted or dry up, the oysters die.

Water and Agriculture

We have learned that New Jersey has many farms. The farmers are finding that their crops grow better if they irrigate them during periods of dry weather. Many farmers

Seabrook Farms Co. Photo

Irrigating farm crops

pump the water for irrigation from streams or wells, onto their crops. As you drive through central and southern Jersey in the summer, you can see this type of irrigation. Most irrigation systems in New Jersey are of the overhead sprinkler type. These throw streams of water 25 or 30 feet in each direction. Many use pumps that furnish 500 gallons every minute. Think of all the water used for this purpose! Irrigation of this sort increases both the quantity and the quality

25

of the crop. Potato crops have been increased from 100 bags per acre to as much as 300 bags per acre by irrigation. These extra 200 bags mean a larger income to the farmer. If all farmers do this, however, there may not be enough water for all. In order to put one inch of water on one acre of land, 27,154 gallons must be applied. Small streams cannot supply this amount of water unless dams and ponds are built to store the water after heavy rains.

Water and Recreation

Camping is a big industry in New Jersey. If you have ever been to camp you know how necessary water is. Without

Standard Oil Co. (N. J.)

Lake Marcia in Sussex County is one of the many lakes of the state used for recreation.

water, a camp would not provide much pleasure. Water is needed for bathing, swimming, fishing, and boating. Of course, there are many other uses of water in camp in addition to the ones mentioned here. These particular ones are always associated with camping, however.

Water for Extinguishing Fires

In all of our cities and towns there are fire departments. The fire departments could not do much to protect our prop-

Warren E. Kruse, Trenton Times

Water is vital in fire fighting.

erty without water. A large fire could destroy an entire city, if water were not available. Every community has to have a large reserve supply for an emergency of this sort. At a recent small fire in Trenton, the firemen reported that they

27

used 32,000 gallons of water to extinguish the blaze. Much more would be required for a large fire.

Water Power

In colonial days, water was used in New Jersey to turn water wheels for grinding corn, sawing lumber, and running mills. Many of the ponds now seen in New Jersey were built in the early colonial days to store water to supply power for these purposes. The city of Paterson, as we have seen, was founded to make use of the power provided by Great Falls on the Passaic River. This water power is still used to produce electricity.

Water and Navigation

In colonial days, before roads were available, streams and rivers were used for travel more than they are now. Produce was moved by canoes, boats, or rafts much more easily than over rough trails through the woods. In the middle of the last century, two canals were built in the state to aid travel by water. The Morris Canal started at Phillipsburg and went to Newark and Jersey City. The boats went through Lake Hopatcong. This canal is no longer used for travel. The Delaware and Raritan Canal went from Trenton to New Brunswick. This canal is now used to deliver water from the Delaware River to industries and communities in Middlesex County and elsewhere.

These are just a few of the many uses of water. All of you could, I am sure, add to this list. These will, however, help you to understand why water is so necessary for our welfare. Each person probably uses about 50 gallons of water daily in the home. If you add to this your share of what industry uses, the amount would be about 140 gallons daily.

Over 593 million gallons per day are used in New Jersey. This amount is increasing each year.

Section 2. THE WATER CYCLE

Many people do not know where the water in wells, springs, and streams comes from. All of the water which we use comes from the clouds. The clouds produce all of the precipitation which we call rain, snow, sleet, or hail. The solid forms of precipitation eventually melt and form water. The water does one of three things when it reaches the earth's surface. It "runs off," "runs in," or "flies off." These processes will be explained in the paragraphs which follow. All of them are familiar to you, I am sure. You have seen them happen after a rainstorm.

In the city, much of the water runs into gutters and then into a storm sewer. The sewer eventually empties into a stream or other natural body of water. In the country, the water runs off the land into streams. These streams often drain into rivers or lakes. Whether the water runs off a city street, a country road, or a farmer's field, it ends up some day in the ocean. All of our streams drain into the ocean eventually. Let us now consider each of the three things that may happen to water.

The amount of water which runs off the land depends upon several conditions. The most important of these are:

1. The slope of the land. If the slope is very steep, more water will run off than if the slope is a gradual one.

2. The amount and kind of vegetation on the land. If the ground is covered with grass, the amount of water that will run off is less than if the land has no grass or other vegetation on it.

3. The nature of the soil. If the soil is very hard, more

water will run off the land than if the soil is soft or sandy.

In New Jersey, about ten or eleven inches out of the total of nearly forty-six that falls as precipitation runs off each year. This is an average for the entire state and will not be

Soil Conservation Service

The Neshanic River in Hunterdon County during a flood period. Pastures and cornfields are flooded.

true for any one particular place. When the amount of run-off is large, floods may occur. Floods do much damage to property, and they often cause loss of life.

In both city and country, some of the water sinks into the soil. The average amount of water that "runs in" or sinks into the earth in New Jersey is just the same as that which "runs off." This is ten or eleven inches, you will remember.

Some of the water which sinks into the soil forms a thin film around the particles of soil, in what is called the "zone of aeration." This means the zone that has air in it. It is the upper part of the soil. More will be said about this in a later paragraph.

The remainder of the water which sinks into the soil goes deeper, into what is called the "zone of saturation." Here the water fills all of the cracks and pores deep in the earth. Water

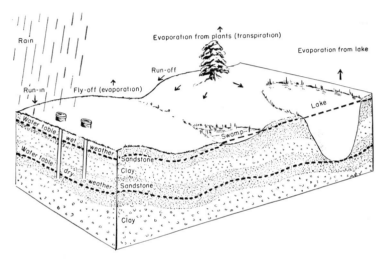

WATER CYCLE AND WATER TABLE

may go down to depths of a half of a mile or more. In the zone of saturation, the soil is always damp or saturated. "Saturated" means that the soil has in it all of the water that it can hold. The upper level of the zone of saturation is given a special name. It is called the "water table." The water table is between the zone of aeration and the zone of saturation.

The water table is very important to us. When the water table is near the earth's surface, the water seeps out to form springs. The water table is at the surface in streams, lakes, and swamps. When it has not rained for a long time, the water table is lowered. After a rain, the water table rises again

31

to a new level. It is also lowered in summer, when plants use a lot of water.

Some water is always held in the deepest parts of the zone of saturation. This is a form of permanent storage. However, most of the water in the zone of saturation moves very slowly through the soil to the nearest stream or body of water, during periods of no rainfall. This water moves only several inches a year, but it supplies the streams with a little water.

The water that sinks into the earth is very important to us. It is the source of all well water. All wells must be dug or drilled below the water table to secure a reliable supply of water. This water that sinks into the earth is the only source of water for streams and rivers during periods when there is no rain. It is the source of all of our water, unless we catch and store surface water in ponds and reservoirs.

The third thing that happens to water is that it "flies off." The scientific term for this is "evaporation." "Evaporation" means that the water is changed to a gas or vapor by the heat of the sun. As a vapor or gas, the water goes into the air. You have all seen this happen, I am sure. Puddles in the street dry up after a summer shower. Clothes put out to dry lose their water by evaporation.

Water that is evaporated comes from three sources. Some of the water is that which was left on the surface of the earth and which did not sink in, or run off, very fast. Some of it is water that went into the zone of aeration and was drawn up again through the soil. Some more of the water is that which was taken into plants through their root hairs. After being used by the plants, much of this water is evaporated by the leaves. As we saw earlier, this process is called "transpiration."

In New Jersey, about twenty-three inches, or half of the

precipitation, is evaporated. This includes water which is evaporated directly and also that which comes from plants by the process of transpiration.

All of the water which is evaporated forms more clouds. From these we get more rain, snow, sleet, or hail, which fall to the earth and complete the "water cycle." That is what the changing from water to clouds and back to water again is called. The water cycle is important to us, for without it, life would not be possible here on earth. The water cycle provides the earth with a continuous supply of clean, fresh water. When water is evaporated, all impurities are left behind. In some parts of our country, the little water that does fall from the clouds is evaporated and carried away. Arizona and New Mexico, for example, are very dry. In New Jersey, we are fortunate in having almost four feet of water come to us each year from the clouds. This water is one of our most valuable natural resources.

Section 3. HOW THE PEOPLE OF NEW JERSEY GET THEIR WATER

Water Supplies in Rural and Suburban Areas

If you live on a farm, or in a suburban area, you may get your water from your own well or spring. The wells must be drilled by state-licensed well drillers. The well is drilled into the earth from thirty to several hundred feet deep. The exact depth depends upon the nature of the earth where you live, and how much water is required. Wells for homes may have a capacity of from five to fifty gallons per minute. Usually homes with wells as a source of water have an electric pump in the basement. This pump goes on and off automatically. It is set so as to go on when the pressure in a tank falls below a certain level.

Many people think that water from wells comes from underground rivers, but this is not true. The water which is brought up in a well in New Jersey is water which fell as some form of precipitation. It has been trapped either in beds of sand or in cracks in the rocks.

In the Appalachian Province, most of the water which sinks into the earth is trapped in openings in the rocks. Wells drilled into rocks are called "rock wells." Such wells do not need screens to keep out sand or dirt. A pipe is put down into the hole that is drilled. This pipe is called a casing, and it is sealed into the top of the rock under the earth. This prevents pollution from surface water. Unless the well driller strikes a suitable crack in the rock, there will not be much water in the well. The very small cracks in the rock are called "joint cracks." Fortunately there are many joint cracks in the rocks of north Jersey.

In some parts of northern New Jersey, glaciers deposited thick layers of sand and gravel on top of the solid rock. Where this happened, water may be found in the sand and gravel. Here wells are drilled only into the sand and gravel and not into the solid rock. These wells are equipped with a casing that has small holes at the bottom. These casings are called screens, and they keep out the sand and gravel and permit the water to enter. Where these wells are drilled, there is abundant water at a low cost.

In the northern part of the state, most wells cannot furnish more than 200 gallons per minute. Some industries need more than this, but for homes it is more than enough.

The best place for drilling wells for large supplies is on the Coastal Plain of the southern section of the state. On the Coastal Plain, there are many beds of sand and clay arranged one on top of the other, like layers of a layer cake. These beds lie in a nearly horizontal position, with a gentle slope toward the ocean and Delaware Bay. The western ends of these beds are exposed at the surface of the ground. These exposures are called "outcrop areas." Rain and other forms of precipitation enter the sand or water-bearing layers or formations at these outcrop areas. The water flows slowly toward the ocean and Delaware Bay at the rate of several inches

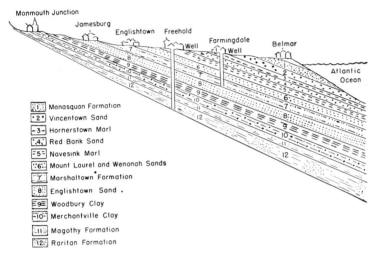

Monmouth Junction
Jamesburg
Englishtown   Freehold
Well
Farmingdale
Well
Belmar
Atlantic
Ocean

[1] Manasquan Formation
[2] Vincentown Sand
[3] Hornerstown Marl
[4] Red Bank Sand
[5] Navesink Marl
[6] Mount Laurel and Wenonah Sands
[7] Marshalltown Formation
[8] Englishtown Sand
[9] Woodbury Clay
[10] Merchantville Clay
[11] Magothy Formation
[12] Raritan Formation

Water-bearing formations on the coastal plain

a year. Many of these sand layers are 100 or more feet thick. The clay beds are tight and do not let the water out of the sand formations.

There are many thousands of wells obtaining water from the sand beds on the Coastal Plain. Some of these wells can supply up to 1,000 gallons a minute. The beds of water-bearing sands on the Coastal Plain are usually called "formations." One of the best water-bearing sands is called the Cohansey Formation. The average tested well in this formation gives 287 gallons of water a minute. The Raritan Formation is another good water-bearing sand. Wells in it produce 242

35

gallons a minute. A third water-bearing sand is the Kirkwood Formation. Wells in this sand give about 220 gallons a minute. Hammonton and Egg Harbor City get their water from this formation.

These formations, or water-bearing sands, hold water under pressure. This pressure is due to the layers of clay. Water does not flow easily through clay. The clay confines the water in the sand just as water is confined in a pipe. Sometimes when a well is drilled into the sand in these formations, the water will rise to the surface of the earth. This is due to the pressure in the formation. Wells in which the water rises to the surface of the earth like this are called "artesian wells."

These water-bearing sands extend out under the Atlantic Ocean. If too much water is pumped from wells, the pressure of the water in the formation will be decreased. This reduction in pressure may permit ocean water to pollute the fresh water. The ocean water comes slowly up the formation. This has happened at Atlantic City and elsewhere.

Some of the wells at Atlantic City are 800 feet deep. The water falls onto the earth near Berlin, New Jersey. Berlin is about forty miles from Atlantic City. It takes the water about 400 years to reach Atlantic City. This rate of one mile in ten years is faster than the rate of movement of water in many places. Water is constantly being pumped for use at Atlantic City, and this increases the rate of flow of the water.

Some wells may be dug rather than drilled. Dug wells are usually shallow wells. When the water table is lowered by drought, a dug well may go dry. Shallow wells are often easily polluted. Like all wells, they should be sealed and constructed to guard against seepage of surface water into them. Most people prefer drilled wells rather than dug wells.

All wells should be located so that ground water cannot bring impurities into them. Even if they are properly constructed, they should be located above any possible source of pollution. Leaks sometimes develop in the casing. If the well is properly located and constructed, well water is excellent water.

New Jersey is a small state, but it ranks ninth in the United States in the quantity of water pumped from its wells. It is the only state that controls the underground water for irrigation.

Soil Conservation Service

Farm pond in Mercer County

Some farms have springs on them. Springs are places where the water table is at the surface, and the water comes out onto the ground. Often this water is piped to a barn or to a house. If the spring is protected from pollution, the spring water may be very good.

37

Many farmers are now building ponds on their property. These make it unnecessary to use so much of the well water. The ponds sometimes receive their water from springs. In some cases the ponds get their water only from rain water or from streams that have been dammed up to hold back extra rain water. The ponds are like little reservoirs. They supply water for fire protection, for irrigation, for livestock, and often for fishing. Ponds are a very good way of saving surface water that would otherwise be wasted.

Water Supplies in Cities and Urban Areas

If you live in a town or a city you probably do not have your own private well. The water which you use in your home is probably bought from the water department of the town or city. There are about 264 separate water supply systems in our state which sell water to individuals or to industries. Of these, 103 are private water companies. The water is usually sold by the cubic foot. One thousand cubic feet equal 7,480 gallons of water. The rates charged for this differ slightly, but in one community in central Jersey, the rate is $2.11 for 1,000 cubic feet. At this rate, one can buy about 35 gallons of water for one cent. A ton of water would cost only a little less than seven cents. This price includes delivery, so you can see that water is not expensive. It is one of the cheapest things we can buy, and it is one of the most necessary of all things we buy.

In the northern half of our state, most of our public water supply is obtained from surface streams and rivers. Flood waters and high stream flows in the winter and spring months are collected and stored in large artificial lakes called reservoirs. These reservoirs, which often look just like natural lakes, store the water for use during hot, dry weather. At these seasons, the flow in the streams is very small.

For a large city, such as Newark, the water supply must be very large. Newark has two sources of supply. One is located on the Pequannock River, which is a branch, or tributary, of the Passaic River. All of the land which drains

N. J. Dept. of Conservation
and Economic Development

Newark Reservoir at Oak Ridge during a dry season

into a stream or river is called a "watershed." The Pequannock Watershed covers 64 square miles. It is located in the Highlands of New Jersey, in Sussex, Morris, and Passaic Counties. The water which is collected and stored in this area goes into four reservoirs on the Pequannock Watershed. From these reservoirs, the water is carried through two large pipelines to another reservoir in Cedar Grove. Here the water is close to Newark, where it is to be used.

The second source of supply for Newark is the Wanaque

39

Reservoir. This is located on the Wanaque River, another branch of the Passaic River. The Wanaque Reservoir is the largest reservoir in our state. It can hold 29,500 million gallons. This reservoir is six and one-half miles long and one mile

North Jersey District Water
Supply Commission

An aerial view of Wanaque Reservoir and Dam

wide. The Wanaque Watershed is located northeast of the Pequannock Watershed and covers 95 square miles. Part of this watershed is in Passaic County, and part of it is in New York State. In addition to Newark, the Wanaque Watershed supplies water to Paterson, Passaic, Clifton, Montclair, Glen Ridge, Kearny, Bayonne, Cedar Grove, and Elizabeth. The water is brought to Newark from the reservoir by large steel pipes, twenty miles in length.

Jersey City is supplied with water by a large reservoir near Boonton. This is on the Rockaway River, another tributary of the Passaic River. Jersey City has another reservoir, known as Split Rock Pond, on the Rockaway Watershed. From this reservoir, water is let flow down the Rockaway River, as required, to keep the Boonton Reservoir full. The force of gravity, or pull of the earth, makes the water flow down into the river.

Some communities in northern New Jersey get their water from wells. East Orange, for example, gets its water from wells which are from 80 to 130 feet deep. Some of the other communities getting water from wells are Plainfield, Westfield, Perth Amboy, Linden, Garfield, and Fair Lawn. There are thirty-five separate water systems supplying water to the northeastern communities of the state.

On the Coastal Plain, most of the water for towns and cities is obtained from wells. The many industries located in this area also get their water from wells. Fifty-three different companies supply the communities in the Delaware Valley area from Trenton to south of Camden. Most of these companies have drilled wells into the sands of the Raritan Formation. You remember that this was mentioned before as an example of a good water-bearing sand. The Raritan Formation is a bed of water-bearing sands ranging from 100 to 500 feet thick. It slopes toward the southeast at the rate of 60 feet per mile. It outcrops, or comes to the surface, on its western end in a narrow band about four or five miles wide. This band extends across the state close to the main line of the Pennsylvania Railroad from New Brunswick to a point east of Trenton. South of Trenton, it extends into Pennsylvania.

Some cities in New Jersey take their water directly from rivers. Trenton takes as much as 40 million gallons a day from the Delaware River. The water is stored in a small reservoir in the city. The average flow of water in the Delaware at Trenton is 8,000 million gallons a day, so ordinarily there is plenty of water for the city. The lowest flow ever recorded at Trenton was in 1954, during the dry summer. Then only 1,350 million gallons a day were recorded. Even this reduced amount was plenty of water for Trenton.

In 1954 Burlington modernized its water system. It drilled wells 50 feet deep on an island in the Delaware River. The water is actually river water which has been naturally filtered by about 35 feet of sand in the river bed. The water is carried by pipes to the city of Burlington. This supplies a total of about 6 million gallons a day, if that much is needed.

We can see from the several illustrations given that there are many ways by which communities can get their water. All of these depend, however, upon the water which falls as rain or some other form of precipitation. In some states, the precipitation is so little that water is not available. In these states, water has to be brought long distances by pipelines from distant mountains. It is stored in large reservoirs. Much of this water comes from snows melting in the spring. California is one state which brings water from great distances.

Section 4. HOW WATER IS PURIFIED

It is very important that the water which we use be pure. If the water is not pure, our health might easily be affected. Many diseases are spread by bacteria in water. Typhoid fever and dysentery are two diseases spread in this manner. Perhaps in your science or health classes you have learned about other diseases which are spread by water.

Water must also look clean. We would not like to use water that was muddy-looking. It is important, too, that water be free from substances dissolved in it which might affect the taste.

The State Department of Health controls the quality of all the public water supplies in New Jersey. This makes it certain that all water sold for public use is clean and pure. The Department of Health must approve the source of such water. It also inspects the water systems, to see that they are properly constructed and maintained in good condition, to protect the purity of the water. The actual measures used to insure clean, fresh water are different for each community. They vary with the source of the water and with the distribution system. Let us see how several communities in New Jersey protect their water supply.

Newark has an excellent supply of water. The city owns over 40,000 acres of land and uses more, which it does not own, on the Pequannock Watershed. Rain falls on this land and runs into streams. The streams carry the water to large reservoirs. The land owned by the city is posted to prevent trespassers. Over five million trees have been planted on this land. It is patrolled by men who clean the 100 miles of streams on it. People live on some of this watershed. A doctor is employed to be constantly alert for diseases which these people may have, since their germs might pollute the water.

Not all cities can protect their source of water in this way. It is too difficult, for example, to control the land along the Delaware River, but water from the Delaware is used by many towns and cities.

Newark maintains its own laboratory, where water is tested daily for odor, color, taste, and the presence of bacteria. The water is treated with chlorine to kill the bacteria. The Newark water supply system is an outstanding example of city ownership of a water supply system which is well managed.

43

In a city like Trenton, which secures its water directly from the Delaware River, additional steps must be taken to insure the purity of the water. Trenton cannot protect its watershed as Newark does. At Trenton, the water is pumped from the river into large tanks, called settling basins. Before it enters these basins, screens remove from it the larger foreign bodies like leaves or pieces of wood. In the settling basins, the heaviest dirt and mud settle to the bottom. A chemical, called

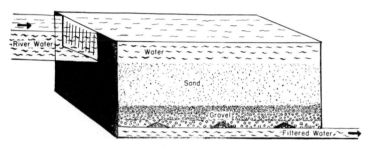

River Water

Water

Sand

Gravel

Filtered Water

FILTRATION BED

aluminum sulphate, is added to the water in these basins. The dirt particles stick to the aluminum sulphate and settle with it to the bottom of the basin or tank. From the settling basins, the water goes to the filter beds. The filter beds consist of three feet of sand and gravel, through which the water passes slowly. The aluminum sulphate which may still be in the water makes a jelly-like mass in the sand. This aids the sand in filtering or straining out any solid matter in the water. It takes about two hours for water to seep through the filter bed. This leaves the water clear. Chlorine is added, to destroy the disease-producing bacteria. Lime is also added, to make the water less acid. Sometimes charcoal is added, to remove odors and to improve the taste. The Trenton water is given one chemical test for impurities and six biological tests for bacteria every day.

44

These two examples show the great effort that is made by large cities to insure the purity of water for our use. Other cities take similar precautions to see that their water is free

North Jersey District Water
Supply Commission

Water treatment plant in Haskell, New Jersey. Here chlorine and copper sulphate are added to the Ramapo River water.

from disease-producing bacteria and is clean. Few cities treat their water exactly the same. The treatment necessary depends upon the source of the water. Some cities, like Plainfield, East Orange, and Bordentown, get their water from wells. This water is already clean, so that all it needs is to have some chlorine added to it, to kill bacteria which might be present. All of us should know what our community does

45

to purify its water. You can find out by visiting the purification plant or by asking one of the town or city officials.

When out camping, one should always make certain that the water used is pure. Boiling the water will kill bacteria.

Exterior of Trenton's modern filtration plant

One or two drops of either iodine or Clorox, added to a quart of water and shaken up with it, will also kill bacteria. It is wisest, however, to use water from sources known to be safe.

Section 5. SOME PROBLEMS RELATED TO WATER CONSERVATION

There is probably about as much rainfall in New Jersey now as there was one hundred years ago. Men who study the weather are not entirely agreed on this point. However, one can frequently read in the newspapers about water shortages we have now which were not known to exist one hundred years ago. The reason for this is not hard to find. Think back to the section of this chapter headed "How We Use Water." How many of the uses mentioned there were not heard of one hundred years ago? Also, think how many more people now live in New Jersey than lived here then. In the first fifty years of this century, the population of the United States doubled. During this time, the use of water increased six times.

New Jersey is becoming more and more built up. Our cities and towns are growing rapidly. This leaves us less area for storing water. Reservoirs require a lot of land. The result is that we are faced with several problems, if we are to have water for all who want it. Some of the problems related to the conservation of water are the following.

Control of Waste

How can we control the waste of water? Several years ago, the reservoirs of New York City were very low. A house-to-house study showed that the repair of leaking plumbing fixtures would save 100 million gallons of water a day. One drop a second from a leaking faucet can waste as much as 175 gallons of water each month. In New Jersey, conditions are probably no different. Each of us could save many gallons of water a day in our homes. Perhaps we would be more careful if our homes all had water meters in them. Homes with water meters pay for the *amount* of water used, in the same way that gas and electricity are paid for. Many of our homes do not have meters. A certain fee is paid for each quarter of a year, regardless of how much water is used. This encourages waste of water. It has been found that people

47

with water meters use about twenty-five per cent less water than is used in homes without water meters. Water conservation should be thought of as an accepted habit for each one of us. It is not an emergency measure only. As our population increases, the need for water will also increase. Most of us could save water every time we get a drink or wash our hands, for most of us are careless about letting the water run unnecessarily.

Re-use of Water

Another problem may soon face New Jersey. This problem is how to re-use water. For example, today most people do not think of re-using water from laundries and industries. Soon there may be developed ways of removing dirt and oil from water which will make it possible to use the water over again. This is already being done in some stores and factories which use large quantities of water for air conditioning. The Division of Water Policy and Supply can require such users of water to put the water back in the ground after use. This prevents the water table from being lowered too much in that area.

Storage of Water

A third, and most urgent, problem in New Jersey is that of how and where to store water. We need more large reservoirs in which to store water which now runs off the ground. This is particularly important in the spring, when rains are heavy and the snow melts. This run-off should be caught and used later in the year. There is plenty of water in New Jersey for all who need it, if the water is stored. Unless we have new reservoirs, new industries will not come into New Jersey. New communities cannot be built, and some of the present users of water may have to do with less.

In 1955, the state bought 54,000 acres of a large section of land in South Jersey, known as the Wharton Tract. Two million dollars were paid for this land. Another 40,000 acres will probably be bought soon. The tract extends over parts of Atlantic, Burlington, and Camden Counties. This land can be used to protect and increase the water supply for the southern part of the state. It represents a very sound investment of the state's money. Just how the land is to be used is not yet decided. Some engineers believe that dams should be built to hold the water in large reservoirs. Others believe that the water should be allowed to seep into the ground. This would fill the water-bearing sands under the earth's surface. The water could then be pumped out from deep wells in other parts of the southern section of the state. This method of storing water would permit more of the land to be used for hunting and fishing and other recreational uses.

Another tract of land which many persons believe is necessary for the development of water supplies in the state is the Round Valley Tract. Round Valley is a 3,500 acre tract of land in Clinton Township in Hunterdon County. Engineers say that it is a natural site for a reservoir. Round Valley would store the flood waters of the South Branch of the Raritan River and possibly of the Musconetcong River. The water would be available to residents of Essex, Middlesex, Somerset, and Union Counties. Water might also be pumped from the Delaware River to help fill this reservoir.

Many other areas which would once have been good sites for reservoirs have now been built up. To use them now would require moving many persons from their homes.

Water Pollution

A fourth problem related to water conservation is how to prevent pollution of streams. Industries and cities are cooperating more than ever before to see that waste water is free from chemicals and bacteria. However, the waters of our rivers and streams are still not as clean and pure as they should be.

The Delaware, the Raritan, and the Passaic Rivers are examples of rivers with polluted water. Education and legislation are two means by which progress will be made. People must realize that great harm is done when water is as badly polluted as many of our streams now are.

Purifying Ocean Water

A fifth problem which may be solved soon is that of finding ways of purifying ocean water cheaply. Our coastal towns may some day find it possible to use water from the ocean, instead of pumping it from wells or collecting it in reservoirs. Ways are being sought to remove the salt and other impurities from ocean water. Congress has provided funds for scientific studies to discover how to do this cheaply.

Ocean water may, of course, be distilled. This is very expensive, because the water has to be heated to change it to a gas. Then the water has to be changed back from the vapor, or gaseous state, to the liquid form.

Another method is now being experimented with. Electrically charged water is filtered through a plastic membrane. A membrane is a thin, skin-like sheet of material. Fresh water has already been produced from ocean water by this method. At present, it costs about sixty cents to make 1,000 gallons of water. If ways are found to reduce the cost so that 1,000 gallons can be produced for about twelve cents, the method will be used to produce water for many people.

Improving Farming Methods to Save Water

Much water that is now allowed to run off into streams could be saved by better farming methods. Another chapter will tell something about methods which prevent soil erosion and also loss of water from the land. This is an important part of farming, about which many farmers need to learn more. When better methods are discovered for saving water, more and better crops will be grown.

Section 6. CONTROL OF WATER SUPPLIES

In New Jersey, the conservation of our natural water resources is under the administration of the Division of Water Policy and Supply. This is one of several divisions in the State Department of Conservation and Economic Development. The Division administers the distribution of water among those who want to use it. The Division cooperates with the United States Geological Survey in studying water problems in the state. The United States Geological Survey is an agency of the government which has engineers in New Jersey. These two agencies measure and keep records of stream flow in our streams. They also measure and record the level of the water in the ground. Studies of these records are made to find out where, and how much, water can be made available.

The policies and decisions of the Division of Water Policy and Supply are made by a nine-man council. Council members are appointed by the governor to represent all sections of the state. The council sits as a court to hear applications for the right to use water. Under our present laws, the council has control over all water supplied to the public from streams or wells. The council also has control over water used from wells for private, industrial, or irrigation purposes, if more than 100,000 gallons a day is pumped in certain areas. This applies only to areas of the state where the water resources are endangered. At present these areas are in Atlantic, Cape May, Essex, Middlesex, and Union Counties. The council has no control over water taken from streams for private, industrial, or other non-public uses. That control is placed in the courts of the state.

The Division also licenses well drillers and issues permits for the drilling of wells. After the well is drilled, the well driller must file a report with the state. The report tells the depth of the well, the size, and the amount of water pumped by the well.

The report also tells the level of the water in the ground and the type of rock under the ground. These reports give the State Geologist valuable information which will assist him in his work. He helps people select sites for drilling wells.

The Division also has control over the building of dams in streams. The construction of bridges, walls, and fills on streams must be approved by the Division. This helps prevent flooding that would occur if construction were not properly done.

Questions of service and water rates are the responsibility of the Board of Public Utility Commissioners. This Board fixes the price for which water can be sold by private water companies. It investigates complaints when service by these companies is unsatisfactory. The Board of Public Utility Commissioners has no control over water supplied by the water departments of towns or cities.

Incodel

The word "Incodel" stands for Interstate Commission on the Delaware River Basin. This Commission is composed of representatives of the states of Pennsylvania, New York, New Jersey, and Delaware. It was established in 1936. The four states represented have a population of more than 30 million people. The Delaware River belongs to, and serves, all these people. The control of the waters of this river is one of the serious problems facing the four states.

Incodel has helped educate people to appreciate the great Delaware. Education has resulted in better use of the land which drains into the river. Improved agricultural practices have kept mud from being carried into the river.

Incodel has a plan for building dams on the Delaware to supply water to all the states represented on the Commission. However, the legislators in all the different states have not yet accepted Incodel's plan.

Cooperation of this sort is very desirable. States must learn to work together to solve common problems, just as individuals must.

Section 7. WATER CONSERVATION AND THE INDIVIDUAL

Individual citizens should all develop an interest in the problems of water supply and control in their community and in the state.

All citizens should support good conservation measures related to water. They must realize that water is not free, and that it needs to be used wisely. If conservation measures are not used, there may not be a large enough supply, at a reasonable cost, for all who need water.

Without water there can be no life. Without water our state cannot prosper.

SOME THINGS TO THINK ABOUT

1. What is meant by the term "water cycle"?

2. Why is the water cycle important to every person?

3. Explain what is meant by the following statement: "Without water there could be no life."

4. Why do more water supply systems in south Jersey than in north Jersey get their water from wells?

5. What are the three things that may happen to rain water?

6. What factors determine the amount of run-off?

7. How do forests and woodlots help regulate stream flow?

8. What are the principal streams in your county?

9. Why are deep, driven wells usually a safer source of water than shallow, dug wells?

10. Why should we have to pay for water, when it falls on the earth in such great abundance?

11. Where does the water in your home come from?

SOME THINGS TO DO

1. Trace on a map of New Jersey the course, until it reaches the ocean, of water which falls as rain near your home.

2. Make a list of all the uses of water that you can think of.

3. See if you can discover any leaks in the faucets or plumbing fixtures of your home, and let your parents know about them.

4. Find out what your family pays for water in a year.

5. Locate on a map of New Jersey as many reservoirs as you can.

6. Ask your teacher to arrange for a class trip to visit the local water purification plant.

7. Look for evidences of pollution in streams and rivers near your home or school.

8. If you live in a town or city where there are large factories, find out how they dispose of their wastes. Do they flow into a stream?

9. Make a list of the lakes, ponds, rivers or streams in your township or in your county.

10. Construct a simple rain gauge by using a large, straight-sided tin can, and measure with a ruler the amount of water that falls in each storm.

11. After a heavy snowstorm, fill a pail with snow, and measure its depth. Melt the snow, and measure the depth of the water. How do the depths of the snow and water compare?

12. Keep a scrapbook of newspaper clippings about water.

13. If you live in a town or city which has a sewage system, find out how the treated sewage is disposed of. Is the sewage put into a stream? Is the sewage treated by chemicals? Does the stream have fish and other wildlife in it?

14. Are there any streams with fish in them near your home? If so, visit them, and see if the streams look clean and free from refuse.

SOME TERMS YOU NEED TO KNOW

Acre—A measure of land (43,560 square feet).

Cell—A small bit of living matter. All living things are made of cells.

Drought—Dryness; a long period without rain.

Evaporation—The changing of a liquid into a gas.

Gravity—The attractive force of the earth which pulls objects "down" toward the earth's center.

Irrigation—The supplying of water to the land by artificial means.

55

Membrane—A thin sheet of material.

Pollution—The act of making impure or unclean.

Porous—Something which permits liquid to go through easily.

Reservoir—An artificial lake for storing water.

Saturated—Soaked through; holding all that it can possibly hold.

Transpiration—The evaporation of water from plants.

Suburban community—A smaller place next to a city.

Urban—A term referring to a city or town.

Watershed—An area of land which supplies water, by drainage on the surface or by seepage, to a stream.

Water table—The level of the underground water. The upper level of the zone of saturation.

Zone of aeration—The upper part of the soil, which contains air.

Zone of saturation—The part of the earth which is saturated with water.

Chapter Three

Our Valuable Soil

Section 1. THE NATURE AND IMPORTANCE
OF SOIL

If you were to ask your friends to name the most important
material things, you would receive many answers. Some
would say air, others would say money, and others, water.
Probably only a very few would mention soil. It is one of
the things which we ordinarily do not think of as important.
However, it is very important to us. From it we obtain much
of our food, clothing, and shelter. Many other things are
obtained from it indirectly. For example, the paper of which
this book is made came from trees which grew in the soil.
Coal, which keeps us warm, was formed from plants which
needed soil in order to grow.

What is the soil? Soil is a relatively thin layer of minerals
and small rock particles, mixed with "organic matter." "Organic matter" means decayed vegetable and animal matter.
Soil, to be good for crops, must contain bacteria and also be
rich in organic materials. The organic matter keeps the minerals from packing, and increases the soil's capacity for holding air and water, which are needed for the plants. We see,
therefore, that soil is not just plain "dirt," as some people
call it.

Soil Layers

Topsoil is the name given to the loose, porous, surface layer of soil. It is usually dark in color and rich in plant food ma-

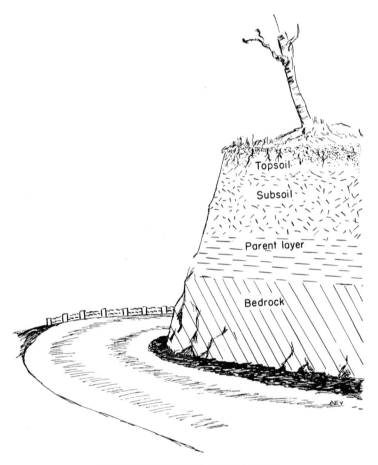

Topsoil

Subsoil

Parent layer

Bedrock

PROFILE SHOWING SOIL LAYERS

terials and bacteria. It is an important layer, because plants grow well in it. Also, it can hold a great deal of water. Plants take out of the soil those things which they need for healthy

58

growth. They can do this only when water dissolves the minerals and food materials.

Farmers and gardeners usually add fertilizers and lime to the topsoil to make it more productive. The topsoil is seldom over ten inches deep. Usually the depth is only five or six inches, and often it is less. When the topsoil is less than six inches, the land will probably be unproductive. Man suffers when the topsoil is gone. Without it he can have no food.

Directly below the topsoil is the subsoil. The subsoil is usually lighter in color than the topsoil. Can you think why this is so? It is also usually less productive.

The third layer of soil is the parent layer. It is called the parent layer because the two other layers come from it. Subsoil and topsoil are formed in the breaking up and weathering of this parent layer. The breaking up goes on faster in some places than in others. The rate depends on the type of material in the parent layer, and on the climate. To produce one inch of topsoil may require a thousand years. Sometimes it may require only five hundred years.

Below the parent layer, there is usually very hard rock. In many parts of the state, this hard rock is right at the surface of the earth. In other places, it is deep below the surface.

We must never forget how valuable topsoil is. Only the topsoil can give and support life. Topsoil is one of our most valuable natural resources.

Certain crops have special requirements. Some plants live best in soils which are acid. Acid soils are also called sour soils. Blueberries and azaleas are examples of plants that grow well in acid soils. Most of the common plants do not grow well in acid soils. To make the soil less acid, lime is put on the soil and mixed with it. We say that lime sweetens the soil. Lime also has the ability to loosen up soils which have too much clay in them. Too much clay makes it hard for the water to go through the soil, and water is necessary for all plant life. Clay also dries in hard lumps and becomes sticky when wet. This makes tilling the soil more difficult. Lime added to the soil will help prevent this.

Soil is sometimes classified according to the size of the particles which compose it. Particles the size of a pea or larger produce a gravelly soil. Smaller particles, each about the size of a grain of sand, make a sandy soil. Still smaller particles, which can barely be seen, produce a silty soil. The very smallest particles, which can be seen only with a microscope, make a clay soil. There are, therefore, four kinds of soil, classified by the size of soil particles.

If a soil has nearly equal amounts of gravel, sand, silt, and clay, it is called a loamy soil or just loam. Depending upon which is most abundant, the soil is called a gravelly loam, sandy loam, silt loam, or clay loam.

Humus

Often we read or hear about "humus." Humus is the natural layer of decaying roots, leaves, and other vegetable and animal matter found on the earth's surface. This decaying organic matter unites with nitrogen and other substances in the ground. Humus gives the soil a dark color. It improves the physical condition of the soil for plant growth. Humus also, later, slowly gives up the nitrogen to plants growing in the soil. Nitrogen is very necessary for plant growth.

Characteristics of Soils

Soils are formed by the breaking down or weathering of rock. Because of this, the soils owe many of their characteristics to the rocks from which they are derived. Some of these characteristics are size of particles, mineral content, and color. Some soils remain near the rock from which they were formed, and others are carried away by rain water or winds.

A good soil for producing a large crop must have several characteristics. It must (1) have sufficient depth and storage capacity for water; (2) have an abundance of plant food materials; (3) have air in it; and (4) crumble easily when plowed or spaded.

Soils differ greatly from place to place. This is due, for one thing, to the differences in the rocks from which the soils were formed. For example, the soil of central New Jersey gets its red color from the iron in it. The iron is abundant in the red shales and sandstones from which the soil is formed. Another cause of soil difference is whether the land is level or hilly. Hillsides usually have thin, poorly developed soils. This is because the soil is washed away as soon as it is formed. Another reason for soil differences is that some soils are older than others. These older soils have developed for a longer time, and more organic matter is found in them. The soils near the Atlantic Ocean, on the Coastal Plain, are more recently formed than the soils farther inland in New Jersey.

It is often difficult to tell just by looking at the soils on the surface, what conditions exist below the surface. A scientist uses a soil auger to bring up soil from below the surface in order that he may study it. A soil auger is like a large corkscrew. It bores into the soil, and when pulled out again, it brings soil up with it. Often two soils may look alike at the surface. The soil auger may show, however, that one soil has a layer of clay several feet below the surface. The sandy soil with a clay layer below the surface will, other things being equal, produce a better crop of potatoes. This is because the clay will prevent the rapid loss of water and keep the sand above it more moist. A good farmer is interested in his soils and knows a great deal about the kinds of soil on his farm. A farmer today has to be well educated. He must

61

learn to observe carefully things that a city person would not ordinarily notice.

Section 2. SOIL EROSION

Soil does not often remain where it was formed. Two of nature's forces are responsible for moving it. They are water and wind. The wearing down of soil and rock masses, by run-off rain water and by wind, is called erosion. The agents of erosion also carry the soil from one place to another. Erosion may wear away an inch of topsoil in two or three years. It took thousands of years to form this soil. When we allow one inch of soil to be lost by erosion, it cannot be replaced in our lifetime. It is lost to future generations, as well as to ourselves.

In New Jersey, water erosion is the most common and most serious form of erosion. Water erosion is of two kinds. These are:

Sheet Erosion. Sheet erosion is the slow removal of a thin layer of topsoil over a large surface. It is similar to removing the pages of a pad of writing paper, one by one. Sheet erosion proceeds so gradually, through the years, that it often is unrecognized for a long time. However, careful observations have shown that sheet erosion in recent years has been responsible for reducing by as much as 20 per cent the quantity of potatoes grown in Monmouth County. Corn, hay, and vegetable crops have been reduced as much as 50 per cent in this same county. Sheet erosion occurs in all sections of the state, even where the ground is almost level. Property owners should guard against it, even though it is a slow process.

Gully Erosion. Gully erosion is the removal of soil through depressions that serve as paths for the run-off water. The

The sheet erosion in this spinach field can lessen the value of the land.

Terraces have helped correct sheet erosion in the same spinach field.

gullies not only hasten erosion, reducing the size of the crops, but they soon make it difficult for a farmer to use machinery in the field. Gully erosion is most active on hilly land. Gullies

Soil Conservation Service

If gullies are not stopped early enough, they can completely ruin a cornfield such as this one in Gloucester County.

increase in size very fast. They may cut right down to solid rock. Once a gully gets started, each rainstorm deepens it.

Some people think wind erosion occurs only on deserts. However, it is very common and destructive in New Jersey. This is particularly true in the southern section of the state, on the Coastal Plain. Wind, blowing over level land, carries the finer, and usually more productive, parts of the soil off the field. This material is deposited where it may not be wanted and will do no good. One day while the writer was driving through Atlantic and Ocean Counties, the wind blew sand with such force that the windshield of his car was badly pitted.

Section 3. CAUSES AND CONTROL OF EROSION

Causes

Erosion is the result both of natural factors and of man's use of land. Some of the natural factors that affect the rate of erosion by water are:

1. The steepness of the slope of the land. Erosion goes on more rapidly if the slope is steep.

2. The ability of the soil to absorb water. Soils which do not absorb water, especially those low in organic matter, are particularly subject to erosion.

3. The amount of rainfall. Erosion is more likely to take place where there are heavy rains than where the rainfall is light.

Probably the most important cause of erosion in many parts of the state is poor land use. Many years ago, farmers raised a large quantity of hay and grains. They left much of their land in pasture. The soil was covered through most of the year, and so it stayed in place. Today less hay is needed, because tractors, rather than horses, do much of the work on farms. Also, many farmers today specialize in one or two cash crops, like potatoes and tomatoes. These crops leave the land bare for longer periods, and more erosion goes on. Also, more trees have been cut off the land to make larger and larger fields. These large fields erode easier than do small fields.

Erosion by wind also is due to lack of plant cover on the

soil. It is most common on the Coastal Plain, where the soil is sandy and loose. However, wind erosion can be seen in Passaic County and other northern counties. Here the land is often left open for growing orchards. The soil between the trees is easily blown away.

Soil Conservation Service

Wind erosion in Burlington County

Both water and wind erosion damage the soil by carrying away the plant food materials which are in the topsoil. The size of the crop is reduced, and the cost of the crop is increased. This is because more fertilizer is required, to make up for the lost plant food materials. If erosion proceeds too far, the entire field may have to be removed from cultivation. Huge gullies make it impossible to work on the land with plows and tractors.

Several years ago, studies were made comparing the crops produced on eroded and on uneroded lands in New Jersey. The following table (Table I) shows the importance of keeping six or more inches of topsoil on the land. Land with six or more inches of topsoil is called "uneroded land" in the table. The column headed "eroded land" deals with land where the topsoil is much less than six inches thick.

TABLE I

(The data for this table were compiled by Harry Slayback and appeared in the Extension Service Bulletin, *Mileposts*, in June 1954.)

| | Quantity of Bushels per Acre | |
Crop	Eroded Land	Uneroded Land
Barley	26	54
Corn	41	67
Potatoes	216	317
Soybeans	4	18
Wheat	18	38

For each of the crops tested, there were more bushels produced per acre on land which was not eroded. Think of how much more money can be earned from land which is not eroded, and which contains rich soil. Also, it must be remembered, uneroded soil probably has in it minerals which will improve the quality of the crop and make it better to eat for people or other animals. There are many minerals which occur in foods in only small traces. Scientists call these secondary elements. Many are necessary for our health. Iron, magnesium, and iodine are examples of the trace elements or secondary elements. Many secondary elements are not present in soils of poor quality.

Soil Conservation Service
Measuring the amount of erosion in this Camden County field

Rules for Good Land Use

Everyone who makes use of any land whatsoever should always think of two rules or principles with respect to the land. This is true whether it be a small yard, a lot in the city, or a several-acre tract in the country.

The first rule or principle is: "Put the land to the use for which it is best fitted." It is silly to try to make a lawn if the slope is too great. Likewise, on a farm some land may also be too steep for crops and should be used for pasture or to grow trees on. Lands differ in the uses to which they should be put.

The second rule is: "Treat the land in accordance with its needs." Your lawn or garden, for example, may be in need of lime. Perhaps it needs fertilizer or peat moss to enrich it.

The addition of sand improves some soils, especially in central New Jersey. Each piece of land is different and requires different treatment. A farmer may need to put in drain tiles to carry off excess moisture on one piece of land. On other fields, he may need to irrigate the land, to supply more water to the soil. These are just a few examples.

Although erosion has caused considerable damage to land in New Jersey, the situation is not hopeless. Each year more farmers are recognizing the need to prevent erosion of soil on their farms.

Methods for Controlling Erosion

Some of the methods of erosion control which are of the most value on farms in New Jersey are the following:

1. *Keeping the soil covered*

Man must try to imitate nature in so far as possible. Whenever a piece of land is left idle, nature covers it with grass, shrubs, and trees. Close vegetation of this sort prevents erosion by (a) slowing down the run-off after a rain; (b) making the soil more porous. This increases its water-holding capacity and reduces run-off. Close vegetation on the soil also retards wind erosion. Planting forest trees on some of the poorer soils is an excellent method of stopping erosion. The leaves of the trees prevent the heavy rain from beating down on the soil. The plant roots make the soil more porous and increase its capacity for holding water. The roots also slow up the run-off after a heavy rain. Growing trees on poor soil provides for a natural restoration of the soil.

Better land can be protected from erosion by keeping it covered with hay crops, such as timothy, alfalfa, and clover. Many farmers now plant clover or other grasses in orchards to prevent erosion there. A good farmer will put in a cover crop, such as alfalfa, clover, or vetch, after he has harvested his cash crop of tomatoes, potatoes, or other crop which would leave the land exposed. The cover crop will hold the soil in place during the winter. Potatoes are a very important cash crop in the central part of New Jersey. Here the land has a slope of from one to five per cent. This means that for every one hundred feet along the surface of the earth there is a fall, or drop, of from one to five feet vertically. On slopes like these, heavy summer rains cause a great loss of topsoil. In the winter, the wind erodes the land if it is not protected by cover crops.

On the dairy farms of the state, corn is often grown. Corn is a poor crop for preventing erosion, because it leaves much of the soil exposed to the wind and the rain. After the corn is harvested in the fall, the land should be planted to another crop to keep it covered.

2. *Contour farming*

Years ago, farmers took pride in plowing a straight row or furrow. Now a farmer tries to plow, cultivate, and plant on the contour. This means that he tries to keep each row or furrow on the level, or at the same height. This may be made clearer to you by an example. Think of a wash basin. Let the sloping sides of the basin represent a piece of land. First, if you let a little water into the basin, the water will rise to a certain height. Now, follow with your finger the line where the water touches the basin on the sides. You have traced a contour or level around the basin. If you add more water, the level will rise on the sloping sides of the basin. Again trace with your finger where the water is in contact with the basin, and you will have another level or contour. A farmer tries to plow along levels or contours like this on his field. By doing this, he makes it harder for the land to be eroded. There is no slope in the furrows, and so water does not easily start erosion by running downhill. Contour furrows hold the water until it soaks into the ground, after a rain.

Soil Conservation Service

Aerial view of a nursery in Mercer County. The young trees in the center are planted on the contour.

3. Strip cropping

Strip cropping consists of seeding the usual farm crops in long bands or strips. These are laid as nearly as possible on the contour or level. They are arranged so that cultivated or tilled crops, like corn and potatoes, are alternated with strips of close-growing crops like hay or grain. Each strip may be about 75 to 100 feet in width, depending upon the slope and the kind of crop to be grown. If the water starts to erode or run off the cultivated strip, it is soon stopped by the nearby

71

strip of the close-grown crop. This is particularly important on hilly land, of course.

Soil Conservation Service

Good land management in Burlington County. The orchard is planted on the contour, and strip cropping is used to prevent erosion.

4. *Building diversion terraces*

If the land is very hilly and must be used for crops, it is sometimes necessary to use farm machinery to build special devices to control erosion. One such device is called a "diversion terrace." A diversion terrace is a broad channel built across the slope and planted with grass. It is several feet wide and carries off the water like the gutter of a house, after a heavy rain. The water is led off to the side of the field where it may enter a stream or woods.

Another kind of terrace is the "crop-land terrace." Grass is not planted in this terrace. The regular crops are planted in rows which run parallel with the terrace. Usually crop-

Sod is cut for use on newly graded watercourses, to prevent erosion.

Sod is laid in watercourses.

land terraces are built closer together than diversion terraces are. There would be more of them on the same amount of land. The water from these terraces is also led to the side of the field.

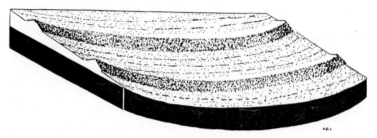

TERRACING

5. *Other conservation practices*

Contour farming, strip cropping, and the building of terraces are good conservation practices. However, good land use requires more than these. For example, it is necessary to keep the soil fertile. After soils have been used for a few years, they lose some of their fertility. A lawn in a city yard may show a poor color. The dark green color of a good lawn is lost, and the grass appears a pale green. There may be patches where the grass grows poorly. A lawn should have fertilizer added to it every two or three years. The grass clippings should be allowed to remain on the ground and rot there. They will add organic matter to the soil.

On the farm also it is very important to maintain soil fertility. There are several ways of doing this. One way is similar to that which was suggested for the property owner in the city. The farmer should return some of the plant food materials to the soil by plowing under parts of the plant. Many farmers, each year, plow under a cover crop such as rye, alfalfa, or clover. This crop rots and increases the

74

amount of organic matter in the soil. Another way of restoring fertility is to return manure to the soil. The manure of cows, sheep, hogs, and chickens contains some of the materials for making plant food. This manure is plowed under and soon decays. The land is then ready for the next crop.

Another important way of keeping the soil fertile is to practice what is called crop rotation. If one crop is grown year after year on the same land, it is constantly taking the same minerals from the soil. It also may affect the way the soil particles cling together. If, however, crops are rotated over a period of years, it is possible for some of the minerals to be restored to the soil. One type of rotation used in New Jersey can be easily remembered by thinking of the word "cows." One year, a farmer plants a piece of land with corn. The second year, the same land has oats on it. The third year it is planted to wheat, and the fourth, to sod. The first letters of the names of these crops spell the word "cows." A good crop for sod would be alfalfa or vetch. These two crops have the ability to replace nitrogen in the soil. Nitrogen is one of the elements which is very necessary and one which is expensive if put into the soil by means of fertilizers.

Lime may also be required on some soils in which crops are to be grown. Lime is not a fertilizer. It is used on soils which contain too much acid. The lime makes the soil less acid, as we have seen. Soils should be tested to see if lime is needed. Your County Agricultural Agent will advise you about this. He will make recommendations for lawns in the city, also.

Erosion control and good land use are important to all of us. If the soil is poor or eroded land is used, the crop produced will be poor in quantity and in quality. The cost of the crop will go up. Even though we live in the city, we will be affected by these two things when we purchase the crop in the store or market. We have seen that erosion can be prevented. Stopping erosion will also help us to save water.

The following table shows the results of an experiment conducted to find out how crops were influenced by contour planting, and how water losses were affected.

TABLE II

Crop Yields as Influenced by Contouring

(Data were compiled by Harry Slayback, Extension Service, 1954)

Crop	Rows Plowed up and down the Slope	Rows Plowed across the Slope
Sweet corn	6,430 ears of No. 1 corn per acre	7,420 ears of No. 1 corn per acre
White potatoes	179 bushels per acre	212 bushels per acre
Corn silage	10 tons per acre	11.4 tons per acre
	8.3 tons of soil lost per acre on corn silage land	1.2 tons of soil lost per acre on corn silage land
	5 inches of water lost per acre on corn silage land	3.1 inches of water lost per acre on corn silage land

From this table, we can easily see some of the advantages of using good agricultural practices. The crop is increased, soil is conserved, and much less water is lost.

Section 4. HOW GOVERNMENTAL AGENCIES ASSIST IN SAVING OUR SOIL

There are many governmental agencies in our state eager to assist residents of the state to use the land more efficiently. Some of these are state agencies, and others are federal.

In every county of our state, except Hudson County, there is a County Agricultural Agent. He usually has an office in the County Court House or other county building. This man is the one to whom you should go first if you have a problem related to agriculture. If you want information about your own garden or lawn soil, he will test it for you and give you advice. If you want to know the best spray for your roses, he will help you. If a disease affects a crop, a farmer can go to him for help. The County Agricultural Agent is a college graduate. His experience in many fields makes him a very helpful person to know. If he does not know the answer to your problem, he will ask for assistance from other sources. He can provide you with many helpful pamphlets and booklets.

Nearly every county also has a Unit Soil Conservationist, who is concerned especially with problems of land use. He is usually located at the county seat, and your County Agricultural Agent will refer you to him if he is the best one to help you.

In New Brunswick, there are several persons to whom one may go for advice and information about agricultural problems. One of these is the Director of the State Agricultural Experiment Station. Another is the Extension Soil Conservationist, located at the New Jersey College of Agriculture at Rutgers University. His office has many pamphlets, booklets, and motion-picture films on soil and water conservation, which can be obtained without charge.

77

To each state there are assigned a number of men who are employed by the United States Government within the Soil Conservation Service. In New Jersey, the State Conservationist and his staff of the Soil Conservation Service are located in New Brunswick. Their services are available to groups of farmers or other citizens interested in soil conservation practices. The State Conservationist also has available, for educational purposes, many films and booklets. Teachers may secure these without charge.

If a farmer decides that he would like to use good conservation measures on his farm, he can get in touch with his County Agricultural Agent, Unit Soil Conservationist, or District Supervisor. The next section will tell you more about the District Supervisor. Men will come to the farm and study it carefully, by means of aerial photographs. They will make a conservation plan which will show each field. Recommendations will be made for the best use and treatment of all fields. These recommendations will be based on soil characteristics, slope, and other factors discussed in this book.

Soil Conservation Districts

In 1937, our New Jersey legislature passed the Soil Conservation Act. Article I of this Act reads as follows: "It is hereby declared to be the policy of the Legislature to provide for the conservation of soil and soil resources of this state, and for the control and prevention of soil erosion."

This Act established a State Soil Conservation Committee. This Committee receives and passes upon all petitions from farmers for establishing soil conservation districts. These districts constitute a governmental subdivision of the state, just as a county is a subdivision of the state. In New Jersey, there are now twelve soil conservation districts. Farmers who wish to organize a district may petition the state Committee and request a hearing in the proposed area. If the Committee approves, then all farmers and landowners in the area vote on the question: "Shall a district be established?" If a majority vote "yes," and these represent 51 per cent or more of the acreage in the proposed district, the Committee will approve the establishment of the district. It will appoint three supervisors as a governing body of the district. The Secretary of State will then formally approve the establishment of the district and record it on his books. After the district is organized, it is managed by the farmers who live there.

The supervisors are then responsible for deciding what work will be done first and for making proposals for wise land use. They secure asssistance for surveys and investigations of soil erosion and the control measures needed. They may acquire machinery for use by farmers. They act as agents for the United States and its agencies in connection with soil conservation projects within the district. They cannot levy taxes or issue bonds, however. The farmers of New Jersey have found these districts to be very useful to them in improving their farming methods.

Wise use of our land is not a problem in which farmers alone are interested. It is a national problem of vital concern to all of us. The prosperity of people in the cities is affected by the degree of prosperity which our farmers enjoy. One cannot prosper without the other. City people need what the farmers produce. Without farmers, we could not have cities. Farmers buy many things from merchants in the city. Each one helps the other. About 13,000 acres in New Jersey have been abandoned because of erosion. Much of this land cannot be reclaimed. It has become permanently unusable for farming.

SOME THINGS TO THINK ABOUT

1. What is soil, and how is it formed?

2. How does the size of soil particles affect the air space in the soil?

3. What things have you seen this week that came from the soil, either directly or indirectly?

4. Do you know of any lawns or fields which show evidences of poor soil condition? What are the evidences?

5. Why do some people believe land to be the most valuable of all natural resources? Do you agree or disagree? Why?

6. Why is topsoil so necessary for a good lawn or a good field?

7. How does farming disturb the balance of nature?

8. How are city dwellers and farm dwellers dependent upon each other?

9. What are some ways by which one can recognize good soil?

10. What are some important reasons why soil erosion should be prevented in both city yards and on country farms?

11. What are several ways by which soil erosion may be controlled?

12. What farm practices may help restore the balance of nature?

13. What is a mulch? How does mulching benefit a garden?

14. Why is making a compost heap in your garden a good conservation measure?

SOME THINGS TO DO

1. Collect specimens of each of the principal types of rocks found in the area. When these rocks disintegrate,

what types of soil will they form? What changes rock into soil? What, in addition to mineral matter, is essential to good soil?

2. Examine a small quantity of soil under a magnifying glass or microscope. Can you distinguish between mineral and organic particles? Note the shape, size, and color of the soil particles.

3. Test soils from different places for acidity, using litmus paper. What types of crops require acid soils? How can acidity be altered? Experiment with this.

4. Collect samples of gravel, sand, silt, clay, and loam, noting where each was found. Did plants grow where each was found? Why? Which size particle will give up mineral plant food most readily? What effect does size of particle have on pore space? (Use a coarse sieve to separate gravel from loamy soil and a fine sieve to separate silt from loamy soil.)

5. Rub samples of different soil types between your fingers. Do they feel gritty? Raise your hand to your ear and rub soil between your fingers. Can you hear anything? What does this indicate?

6. With a spade, determine the depth of the topsoil in several places. Is it the same depth in all places? Why?

7. With a piece of string, lay off a square foot of soil in two or more locations. Count the number of insects, worms, and other animals within the upper inch of soil. Are they equally numerous in all types of soil? Why?

8. Compare the color, texture, structure (looseness or compactness), and depth of topsoils in several places near a stream bed and in an upland location. Describe the type of vegetation growing in each.

9. Use four quart jars or tin cans. Fill them with equal quantities of gravel, sand, silt, and clay. Weigh each, and

81

then saturate each with water and reweigh. What are the results? Which soil held the most water? Why?

10. Place equal amounts of different kinds of soil in separate jars. Fill each jar with water, shake, and allow to stand for a few hours. What is the order in which the solid material settles out of the water?

11. Place some sandy soil, loamy soil, and clay soil in separate cans. Add water to each and stir until each is in a soupy condition. Allow each to stand until it is very dry, and then describe the condition of each. Which would make the best garden soil? Why?

12. Get two small wooden boxes of the same size. In one, put about seven inches of black soil. In the other, put six inches of the same black soil, and cover it with one inch of ground limestone or other white or light-colored soil. Put a thermometer about three inches under the soil in each box. Place both boxes in the sun, and take readings every half hour for several hours. Record the temperatures. Was the temperature in each box the same? Why? What color soil might be best for an early spring garden?

13. Dig two holes, one in bare ground and the other in ground under grass or tree cover. Which hole shows more moisture? Why?

14. After a heavy rain, look at soil materials that are washed into highways, road ditches, or gutters. Where did they come from? Why are they there?

15. Visit a farm, and see what soil and water conservation measures are being used.

16. Build a model farm which illustrates good conservation practices.

17. If there is any abandoned land near your school, study its condition. How could it be restored?

18. Study roadside plantings in your neighborhood, and

find out what plants are used to prevent the erosion of soil on roadbanks.

19. After a heavy rain, visit a nearby farm and see if there was erosion in potato or tomato fields. Did these fields erode more or less than pasture land or land in hay? Why?

SOME TERMS YOU NEED TO KNOW

Cash crops—Crops sold for cash at the end of the growing season, instead of being kept on the farm to feed animals or people.

Clay—An earthy material used to make pottery and bricks. Pure white clay is called kaolin.

Contour—On the level or at the same elevation.

Cover crop—A close-growing crop, such as alfalfa, clover, or other grass, which will cover the soil and protect it from erosion.

Crop rotation—Planting a different crop on the same land each season or year for several years.

Crop yield—The quantity of crop harvested or raised in a season.

Erosion—The wearing away of the land and the moving of soil by water, wind, or some other natural agent.

Fertile—Rich in plant food materials. Fertile soil has the ability to produce a very good crop.

Fertilizer—A substance put on the soil to enrich it by supplying needed organic or mineral matter.

Gully erosion—The cutting into the soil by water so that deep depressions or gullies develop.

Humus—The natural layer of decayed vegetable and animal matter found on the earth's surface in good soil.

Loam—A rich soil made up of equal parts of gravel, sand, clay, and silt.

83

Minerals—Substances, other than animal or vegetable, occurring naturally and having definite physical and chemical characteristics.

Neutralize—To destroy or change the properties of a substance.

Organic matter—Materials that now do have or once did have life.

Parent layer—The layer in the soil from which other soil layers were formed.

Rocks—Solid natural substances, other than animal or vegetable, covering a large area of the earth's surface. A rock may be composed of a single mineral or may be a combination of several minerals.

Sheet erosion—The gradual wearing away of the land by water or wind. The land is removed in sheets, just as the pages of a writing pad are removed.

Silt—Very fine particles of earth.

Soil—The loose surface of the earth, in which plants grow.

Soil auger—A tool used to bring soil up from the lower levels to the earth's surface.

Strip cropping—The growing of crops in long, narrow belts or strips.

Subsoil—The layer of weathered material which underlies the surface soil.

Terrace—A strip of nearly level land on a slope, to hold water or to guide its run-off to prevent erosion.

Topsoil—The top layer of organic, fertile earth.

Weathering—The natural process of softening and breaking up of rocks.

Chapter Four

Our Green Acres

Section 1. THE TREES OF NEW JERSEY

Many people who have lived in New Jersey all of their lives would be surprised if they could fly above the state. There would be, below them, many more trees than they might expect to see. Actually, about 45 per cent of the entire state is

Newark News

A beautiful view of the wooded hills of Passaic County

covered with trees. Some of these are on wood lots of farms, and others are in state forests and parks. Many are found in our cities and towns, on streets, in yards, and in parks. These trees are a very important natural resource.

Trees of the Appalachian Province

The greatest number of trees in the Appalachian Province of the northern part of our state are "deciduous." Deciduous

Evelyn M. Carlile

A sawmill near Crosswicks in Burlington County

trees are trees whose leaves all fall off each season, such as the oak, the maple, the ash, the hickory, and the birch. These are often called "hardwoods." It is not the purpose of this book to help you to identify the trees or other living things mentioned in it. There are many good guides to plants and animals which can help you do this. Perhaps you will want to use one of these guides to assist you to identify some living things that are particularly interesting. The red oak tree, for

Evelyn M. Carlile

Large oak logs are loaded in Mercer County for hauling to a sawmill.

example, has been designated as the state tree for New Jersey. Perhaps you will want to be able to identify it.

Lumbering was once an important occupation in northern New Jersey. However, today, due to the cutting of the trees to make land available for farming, and due to the growth of residential areas, the number of large trees has decreased very much. Today lumbering is not as important as it was one hundred years ago. However, there are still over one hundred sawmills in New Jersey.

87

Oak trees are still cut in our state for use in shipyards where barges and ships are built. During the last World War, many submarine chasers and landing barges were built in New Jersey shipyards from oak cut in our state. Oak and maple trees

Power saws have replaced the hand saws in New Jersey lumbering operations.

are also used in the copper-smelting industry of the state. Copper ore contains many impurities. The ore is heated until it becomes a hot liquid. Long pieces of oak and maple wood are burned in this hot liquid ore. This causes the impurities to be removed from the ore. They are burned with the wood. Copper ore is smelted around the Perth Amboy area in Middlesex County. Very straight, long oak trees are cut to make piles. Piles are used in making ferry slips, the places where ferry boats dock. Piles are also driven into the ground to form solid foundations for bridges. The poorest quality of oak wood is sawed into lumber to make props and supports for

Seabrook Farms Co. Photo

Manpower is still important in lumbering.

mines. Some of our oak is used for this purpose in the zinc mines of Sussex County and in the coal mines of Pennsylvania.

Yellow poplar and sweet or red gum trees are used to make fruit baskets. There are basket factories at Bridgeton, Swedesboro, and Belle Plain. Yellow poplar is also used to make veneer for airplane construction. Veneer is a thin layer of wood glued on top of another kind of wood.

Hardwood trees also furnish us with good wood for fuel. It is sawed into short lengths for fireplaces.

89

Trees of the Coastal Plain

The eastern part of the Coastal Plain, in New Jersey, is a region of pine trees. Here there are over 2,000 square miles of pine forests. The trees, for the most part, are a mixture of scrub pine, pitch pine, shortleaf pine, and some oaks.

In the swampy sections of the Coastal Plain grows the southern white cedar tree. This is a valuable tree for making posts. It is also very useful for converting into lumber for use in boat building. The swampy sections also contain red maple, black gum, and sweet or red gum trees.

Much of the upland, or drier part of this section, has been burned over frequently by forest fires. These fires have caused the trees to become stunted and in poor condition to produce good lumber.

Within the Pines, there is a section known as the Plains. Here the trees are extremely stunted and grow only five or six feet tall. The Plains are on both sides of Highway 72, between Chatsworth and Tuckerton. The Plains are the result of repeated forest fires which destroyed the vegetation.

A large amount of the pine wood from the southern part of the state is used to make pulp for the manufacture of roofing felt. The wood is cut into short lengths and delivered to the pulp mill, where it is ground up into small pieces and cooked with liquid chemicals. The soft mass which results from this cooking is called pulp. There are mills to handle wood for this purpose at Gloucester City, Little Ferry, Rahway, Manville, Camden, and Perth Amboy.

Most of the oaks which grow in with the pines on the eastern part of the Coastal Plain are of poor quality. Good, strong, tall oak trees grow from acorns. In the Pines, the oak trees grow mostly from sprouts which come up from the roots of trees that were cut down or burned. The "sprout oak," as it is called, does not grow tall and straight. Foresters do not like to see it grow in with the pines, because it produces a poor quality of lumber. Some of the common oak trees that grow here are the scrub oak, blackjack oak, and post oak.

Seabrook Farms Co. Photo

Logging in South Jersey. Logs are dragged to the trucks by tractors.

In South Jersey, on the Coastal Plain along the Delaware River Valley, there is a strip of very fertile land. This includes parts of Burlington, Camden, Gloucester, and Salem Counties. The trees that grow in this very fertile soil are very tall. They include such species as tulip, willow, pin oak, scarlet oak, white oak, and swamp oak. These all grow on the drier parts of the area. In the moist parts of this valley, there are sycamores, elm, sweet gum, black gum, and birch trees.

91

State Forests and Parks

The state has acquired about 80,000 acres of woodland, which have been set aside for state forests and state parks. As our population grows, we shall need much more land for this purpose.

As the terms are used in New Jersey, there is not much difference between a state forest and a state park. State forests are intended for many uses, such as producing lumber, conserving water, and providing recreation, including hunting and fishing. State parks have more limited uses. Hunting is not permitted in state parks. State parks provide recreation of other sorts and are places where plants and animals can be conserved.

There are in New Jersey ten state forests and twenty-two state parks. These are well distributed over the state. They are intended to serve all of the citizens of our state for many years in the future. Each year, about two million persons visit the state forests and parks.

Section 2. HOW OUR FORESTS AND WOODLANDS SERVE US

The wooded areas of the state serve us in many ways. Most people do not realize how much the woodlands contribute to our way of living. A few of the most important ways in which wooded areas serve us are discussed in this section.

1. *Forests and wood lots provide much valuable wood.*

We have already seen that the trees of our state furnish wood for many purposes. Some trees, such as the oak, provide wood for building boats. Others, like the poplar, provide wood for basket making. We use the wood from the oak and hickory trees in our fireplaces at home and at camp. Pulp, for making roofing felt, is produced in large quantities. It is estimated that the value of our state's wood products is about eight million dollars a year.

2. Trees restore soil fertility.

The leaves and the small twigs which fall from trees soon decay. These materials add organic matter to the soil. You will remember that when we studied about soil, we found that organic matter was very necessary. Most wooded areas have a thick layer of decaying vegetation on the ground. This restores the fertility of worn-out soil.

3. Trees prevent erosion and hold water in the soil.

The many small roots of trees and the organic matter on the ground hold back rain water after heavy rains. This is important for two reasons. First, the soil is not easily eroded when the roots and organic matter slow down the movement of the water. Streams in wooded areas seldom have much mud in them. Second, we need the water in the ground. If all the excess rain water runs off after a heavy rain, we experience floods. Floods waste water. If the soil has roots and organic matter in it, the water is released slowly, and there are no floods. Springs and streams would, in many places, dry up if trees were all destroyed. We saw in Chapter Two that we do not now have enough reservoirs. Without forests and wood lots, we should need even more reservoirs than we do now. They are very expensive to build and to maintain. It is cheaper and better to let our forests and wood lots work for us by storing water and releasing it to the streams gradually. Trees help prevent floods and the waste of water in another way. Their shade often delays the melting of snow in the spring. The snow, therefore, melts more gradually on land which has plenty of trees, and this prevents floods. The water is saved until it is needed later.

4. *Wooded areas benefit wildlife.*

In another chapter, we shall learn about the wildlife of our state and its importance to us. Without forests and wood lots, we should not have as many wild animals as we do now.

John Wolbarst

The William L. Hutcheson Forest Ecological Project, formerly Mettler's Woods, in Middlesex County. This is one of the oldest stands of timber in New Jersey.

Many of the animals of the woodlands and forests supply us with food and recreation. The trees supply food and shelter for these animals.

5. *Forests have great recreational value.*

Thousands of residents of New Jersey and nearby states enjoy going into the forests. In some of our state forests, there are cabins and camp sites which can be rented for a very moderate charge. Many persons use these each year. Bulletins describing these state forests and parks may be obtained from the State Forester, State Department of Conservation and Economic Development, Trenton, New Jersey. If you are interested in a particular state forest or state park, write to the superintendent of that forest or park for a bulletin describing it.

Many of the forests and parks have lakes for swimming. Most of them have fireplaces and picnic tables. To those who love the out-of-doors, the forests serve as an escape from the crowded cities. Relaxation such as a forest provides is good for all who live at the fast pace of the city. Each of us should try to spend a day or two in the open, every once in a while. The word "recreation" means to refresh or give fresh life. Our forests and parks do this for us. Forests add to our health and happiness. New Jersey needs more forests and parks than it now has. As our population increases, there will be even more need for recreational facilities. Today, on many weekends in the summer, our parks and forests are overcrowded. Lakes that were built to accommodate several hundred people often have several thousand people trying to get in them.

6. Forests serve as laboratories.

A laboratory is a place in which one carries on experiments. An experiment helps us to find new and better ways of doing things and new answers to our problems. Foresters are always carrying on experiments on our woodlands. They are trying to find out how water can best be held in the soil. They are experimenting with new ways of controlling forest fires. Experiments are carried on to find how insects and diseases which affect trees can best be controlled. Many of these, and other, experiments could not be carried on in any place other than in a forest or wood lot.

Section 3. GOVERNMENTAL AGENCIES AND OUR TREES

State Foresters

To manage woodlands wisely requires knowledge and skills of a special kind. Not every property owner has such knowledge and skills. The state employs trained foresters to help a property owner who has a wood lot. These foresters also manage the publicly owned woodlands. The Bureau of Forests, Parks, and Historic Sites is a part of the Department of Conservation and Economic Development. This Bureau employs the trained foresters, who will come to a person's home and advise him about his wood lot. The property owner will receive from one of them suggestions concerning which trees should be cut for sale and which should be left to grow for a longer time. The forester will put blazes on the trees which should be cut. A blaze is a place where the bark of the tree is removed. The letters "N.J." are stamped on the blazes to show that the trees so marked should be cut. The forester will give to the owner of the land an estimate of the quantity of lumber in his wood lot. He will also recommend to him a reliable "timber agent." A timber agent is a man who knows about lumbering, and who will help the owner sell his trees to a lumber dealer. The timber agent receives a commission for his services. That is, he is paid according to the money received for the timber sold. The timber agent shows the trees to the lumber dealers. He receives their bids, which name the price they are willing to pay for the lumber, and he prepares the sales agreements. When the lumbering operation starts, the timber agent supervises the cutting. He sees that only those trees marked with the "N.J." stamp are cut. He also sees that other trees are not damaged unnecessarily. A property owner who uses the services of a state forester

N. J. Dept. of Conservation
and Economic Development

Good forestry practices in North Jersey. Some trees are left after a light cutting to provide seeds.

and a timber agent usually receives a higher price for his timber than he would otherwise receive. Also, he suffers less loss from careless lumbering practices. Usually he has enough young trees left so that within about twenty years he can harvest another crop of timber. Foresters recommend selective cutting. That means that only the large trees are cut

97

at any one harvesting, leaving the others for the future cuttings.

The state foresters also help the public in another way. They write pamphlets and publish articles which are available to interested persons. These discuss such things as the care of trees, proper planting methods, and related topics.

N. J. Forest Fire Service

Poor forestry practices. The branches and wood on the ground are a fire hazard.

The pamphlets may be obtained by writing to the State Forester, Department of Conservation and Economic Development, Trenton, New Jersey. The State Forester will be glad to answer questions from property owners about trees. Groups of people may also arrange to have a forester come to them for a lecture on forestry.

As we have seen, foresters working for the state are always carrying on research on new methods for doing things related to trees and forests.

The Bureau of Forestry, Parks, and Historic Sites operates a tree nursery at Washington Crossing State Park. This was established in 1926. Here, several kinds of trees are raised and sold to property owners. To be allowed to buy these trees, a property owner must own at least ten acres of land. He must agree not to resell the trees or to use them for merely ornamental purposes. The trees are sold for about eight dollars for a thousand trees, if they are three years old. For younger trees, the price is slightly less. It is a beautiful sight to see over seven million young trees at the nursery. The trees raised there are chiefly the following kinds: Norway spruce, Douglas fir, white pine, hemlock, Austrian pine, loblolly pine, and black locust. Each year, almost two million trees are shipped from this nursery to be planted all over the state.

Each of the state forests and parks is under the control and supervision of a state forester.

United States Foresters

In addition to the state foresters, there are in New Jersey several United States foresters. These men cooperate with the state foresters in carrying on research. Some of them live right in the forest all year around. In our largest state forest, Lebanon State Forest in Burlington County, there are several interesting experiments being carried on by these two groups of foresters.

One experiment that these men are working on is to find out how best to encourage pine trees to grow there instead of oak trees. You remember, it was said earlier, that oak trees in South Jersey often grow from sprouts. These do not become good, sturdy trees. Pine trees will grow well in southern Jersey if they are not crowded out by the oaks. Experiments and research have shown that pine trees grow best in "mineral soil." A mineral soil is one that is sandy and lacking in organic matter. Most plants need organic matter in which to grow, but this is not true in the case of pine trees. Pine seedlings have very short roots and do not have a very large supply of food in the seed. Short roots cannot get through the thick layers of organic matter, and the seedlings die. To get rid of the organic matter, so that pines can grow easily, the foresters are experimenting with "prescribed burning." Prescribed burning means that a small fire is deliberately set and used as a tool to improve some unsatisfactory condition. Such fires must be kept small and light, so that they do not damage tree seedlings which the foresters want to keep in the forest. Prescribed burning is usually done only in the winter months, when the ground is damp. This type of fire destroys the leaves and litter on the surface but does not kill tree seedlings. Prescribed burning should only be done under the supervision of an experienced forester. Equipment for extinguishing the fire must always be close by. All fires can be dangerous if not properly controlled. Prescribed burning is still in the experimental stage and should not be used by every property owner.

The above two examples show the type of experiments that are now being carried on in our forests. Of course, there are many others being carried on at all times.

Municipal Shade Tree Commissions

In towns, cities, and counties, there are usually some governmental agencies concerned with trees. These agencies are usually called Shade Tree Commissions. The Shade Tree Commissions give advice to the residents of the town, city, or county. They suggest good trees to plant on roads and streets and in yards. Often the trees are sprayed for insects and fungus diseases by the employees of the Shade Tree Commission. When it is necessary, these employees trim or prune trees. The members of these Commissions regulate the planting and care of ornamental trees and shrubbery on public roads and in public parks. Perhaps you can find out if your town or city has such a Commission and what its duties are. In a town or city, the office of the Shade Tree Commission is usually located at the Town or City Hall. If there is a County Shade Tree Commission in your county, it is located in the County Court House.

The Department of Conservation and Economic Development has prepared a pamphlet entitled *The Laws of New Jersey Relating to Shade Trees.* This will tell you more about the work of the municipal agencies mentioned here. The pamphlet may be obtained by writing to the State Forester in Trenton.

Section 4.   SHRUBS AND SMALLER PLANTS

We have just learned in the preceding section about some of the trees of our state. In addition to trees, there are many smaller plants that help to make our landscape green and beautiful in the summer season. Shrubs differ from trees by being usually less than ten feet tall and by not having a definite crown shape such as trees usually have. Shrubs and smaller plants help hold water in the soil and prevent erosion just as trees do.

New Jersey has a rich collection of plant life. In respect to plant life, we are a border state. There are some plants here that are usually found in southern states. There are others that are usually found in northern states. Famous botanists have come from all over the United States to study our plants. They are particularly interested in those of the Pine Barren area of the Coastal Plain. Unfortunately, many of the plants of the state are rapidly disappearing. New communities are being developed constantly. These and the many new highways have resulted in the destruction of many interesting native plants.

There is not space in this book to list all of the plants that are found in New Jersey. Mention will be made, however,

Dorothy M. Compton

Ground pine is one of the plants which is in need of particular protection in our state.

of some that are in particular need of protection, for this book is concerned with the conservation of our natural resources. The following are plants that should be given special attention. Efforts should be made to see that they do not disappear entirely from our woods and fields. They are azalea, bittersweet, gentians, ground pine, holly, lady-slipper, mountain laurel, orchids, pitcher plant, rhododendron, and sundew. Perhaps New Jersey should have laws to protect these and other plants. However, laws by themselves are insufficient, unless every citizen has a strong desire to respect these laws. Each of us should learn to recognize and protect these plants.

There is one law, passed in 1926, about which we should all know. This law makes it illegal for any person to remove or damage a plant without the permission of the property owner on whose land the plant is growing. Many persons do not know about this and believe that they can pick any plant or shrub in a field or woods. This law applies to any tree or shrub or flower, although it stresses holly, laurel, wintergreen, rhododendron, and ground pine.

In 1936, another law concerning plants was passed by the state legislature. This law gives added protection to bittersweet, which was then becoming scarce. The law makes it illegal to sell, or take for the purpose of selling, any bittersweet growing in the wild. There is a ten-dollar fine for each offense. This law is enforced by the Division of Fish and Game.

Wild flowers die soon after they have been picked. We should all learn to appreciate and enjoy the beauty of plants in the fields and woods. Even when the entire plant is transplanted to a home garden, it will often die. Usually the soil or the light is different from that where the plant originally lived.

One plant about which all New Jersey residents should know more is the violet. This has been chosen as the state flower for New Jersey. Fortunately, it is one of several species of flowers that can be picked quite freely. This is so because it has several different methods by which it reproduces itself. Each year, new leaves and flowers appear from a root which lives from season to season. Also, the violet has many leaves on stems that are separate from the flower stems. The leaf makes the food for the rest of the plant, and even if the flower is picked, the leaf is apt to be left, because it is on a separate stem. Most people never see the little flower buds on the violet plant, close to the ground, which produce many seeds. Many people do not know they are there, and since these little buds are not attractive, they are not picked. Thus, they are left to produce seeds for another year. Because it has several means of reproduction, there is little danger of the violet disappearing, as long as there are fields in which it may grow. Most plants are not so fortunate as the violet and therefore need our help in order to continue to be with us. Let us, therefore, give them all of the protection that we can.

If you are seriously trying to protect our wild flowers and shrubs so that all may enjoy them, you will follow certain rules. These are not all laws, but all are good rules to follow. They are:

1. Pick plants and flowers only if you have the permission of the owner of the land on which they are growing.

2. For every flower that you pick, leave at least ten more unpicked. These will help to supply seeds for another year.

3. Cut all stems and branches with a sharp knife or pruning shears, instead of breaking them off. When cutting, be careful not to tear the bark of the tree or shrub. Bacteria and fungi which cause diseases in plants may enter the plant through cuts and wounds in the bark.

4. Collect only as many flowers or branches as are really needed and can be cared for properly.

5. Where possible, pick only the blossom, rather than the entire plant. Allow the leaves to remain on the plant.

6. If you are camping out or building a picnic fire, use only dead, dried wood for the fire. Do not build the fire too close to living trees or shrubs. Remember that a permit is required for fires that are built in wooded areas. Before going

out camping, you should read carefully the next chapter of this book. It contains rules for campers who build camp fires.

SOME THINGS TO THINK ABOUT

1. Of what value are the state forests and parks to people who live in large cities?

2. In what ways is a forest more than a collection of trees?

3. Of what value is a forest, other than to supply wood for commercial purposes?

4. How do you think that the attitude of early settlers in our state toward their forests compared with our present-day attitude? Why?

5. What does it mean to speak of harvesting timber as a crop?

6. Why are publicly owned forests desirable in a conservation program?

7. Why, if one is to pick flowers wisely, should one know how the plant on which a flower is growing reproduces?

8. What are some plants in your area of the state which, in your opinion, do not need any particular protection? Why?

9. Why is the violet less likely to be completely lost to our state than some other plants?

10. What is the difference between deciduous and evergreen trees?

SOME THINGS TO DO

1. Locate on a large map of the state all the state parks and forests.

2. From the encyclopedia, or other library reference, find out about the chestnut blight which destroyed all the state's chestnut trees early in this century. What other trees are in similar danger?

3. Make a list of the reasons why you think forests are important natural resources.

4. Visit a state forest or park, and report to the class about your trip.

5. Write an article for your school paper or class paper on the subject, "Why We Need More State Forests in New Jersey."

6. Secure bulletins from the State Forester, and report to your class about the content of these bulletins.

7. Make a list of the various forms of wildlife that depend upon the forest for their existence.

8. Collect pictures of trees and plants mentioned in this chapter.

9. Make a collection of the articles that appear in the daily newspaper about the plants of New Jersey.

10. Learn about the Boy Scout or Girl Scout Conservation Programs.

11. Make a collection of the leaves of trees in your community, and press these leaves in a heavy book between sheets of paper.

12. Make blueprints of some common tree leaves.

SOME TERMS YOU NEED TO KNOW

Decaying—The gradual breaking down of a substance.

Deciduous—The term applied to trees whose leaves die at about the same time each year.

Evergreens—Trees whose leaves do not all die or fall off at the same time.

Experiment—A trial made to prove or disprove an idea. A practical test to find the answer to a problem.

Mineral soil—A soil that is sandy and does not have much organic matter in it.

Oxidation—The combining of a substance with oxygen.

Prescribed burning—A light fire that is started intentionally and used as a tool to improve an unsatisfactory condition.

Smelting—The melting of ores of metals to extract the pure metal.

Sprout oak—Oak trees which have grown from roots of trees that were cut or burned, and not from acorns.

Veneer—A thin layer of wood glued to another layer of wood to add beauty or to give strength.

Chapter Five

Our Black Acres

Section 1. INTRODUCTION

In the last chapter, we learned a little about our green acres. That is what we called the land covered with living trees and shrubs. Unfortunately, many of these green acres become "black acres." You would better understand the meaning of this term if you were to drive through a section of our state that had experienced a forest fire. After the fire, everything looks dirty, black, and lifeless. It gives one a feeling of sadness to see land like this. Black acres are not natural resources, of course. They are the result of careless use of our resources. They are the result of fires and of diseases of trees which fires may have made possible.

Section 2. CAUSES OF FOREST AND WOOD LOT FIRES

As we know, New Jersey is a small state. In spite of its small size, it has a large number of forest or wood lot fires each year. For the past ten years, the average number of fires a year has been nearly 1,500. Most of these fires are in South Jersey. There are five times as many on the Coastal Plain as there are in the Appalachian Province. One reason for the difference in the number of forest fires in North and South Jersey is the difference in the kinds of trees in their forests.

In South Jersey, there are more pine trees than in North Jersey. The needles of pine trees burn more easily than do the leaves of other trees. Also the soil is very sandy on the Coastal Plain. The rain seeps into the sand, leaving the surface dry. The leaves and other materials on the surface burn

Forest-fire fighters on the fire line

easily because they are dry. Another reason is that more people travel on the roads through the forests in South Jersey than in North Jersey. Probably if we did not have such a good road system through the forests there would be fewer fires. We have already learned New Jersey has a large population. When five million residents and the visitors to the state travel as much as they do, we have to expect fires. However, too many of our citizens are thoughtless and careless. They do not realize the danger, for example, of throwing

109

a lighted cigarette or match out of a car window. It is care-lessness of this sort which turns over 10,000 acres each year from "green acres" to "black acres." In 1954, a law was passed by our legislature making it illegal to throw a lighted object out of an automobile or other vehicle. Unfortunately, not all persons remember to obey the laws designed for their pro-tection.

The most common causes of forest or wood lot fires in New Jersey and the percentage of fires caused by each are shown below.

TABLE III

Cause	Percentage of Fires
Smokers	57
Burning trash and brush	15
Railroad trains	13
Incendiary (started intentionally)	10
Miscellaneous	4
Campers	1

Many people think lightning starts forest fires. This is truer in the western United States than it is in New Jersey. In our state, only about one fire a year is caused by lightning. The reason for this is that in New Jersey, lightning is usually accompanied by heavy rains. This is not so in the western states. Here the rains would put out any fire which might start. Also, fires do not start here because the trees and leaves are often wet from the rain that came before the lightning.

The accompanying table shows that most of our woodland fires start as a result of human carelessness. To start a fire, a temperature of about 800 degrees Fahrenheit is needed. In nature this temperature is not easily reached. It is usually man who produces it. Someone has said that there are only three main causes of fire: men, women, and children. All of us should guard against carelessness with fire, because the effects are very serious when fires are started and get out of control.

Section 3. EFFECTS OF FOREST AND WOOD LOT FIRES

1. *Fires cost money.*

During the summer of 1954 there were some of the worst fires on record in our state. During one week it cost the state about $15,000 to pay fire fighters. In addition, there was damage done to fire-fighting trucks which cost more money. Equipment had to be replaced, and this cost still more money. There was also a loss of at least $250,000 in buildings and timber.

2. *Fires destroy timber.*

Fires destroy the wood in a forest or wood lot. This means a loss of money to the owner of the trees, because he cannot sell damaged wood. If the fire does not burn up a tree altogether, it may cause wounds to develop in it. Wounds leave scars which make the wood less valuable for lumber.

3. *Fires weaken the trees' resistance.*

Wounds caused by fire are dangerous, for through them insects and fungi may enter which will damage the tree. Of course, healthy trees may also be affected by these enemies.

Fungi are very small plants. They cause most of the major losses from disease in trees. Fungi may either kill or merely weaken a tree. Weakened trees are easily blown over by strong winds. They also are easily affected by insects. Fungi are spread by insects, birds, man, and wind.

A fungus brought from Asia in about 1904 has destroyed all of the large chestnut trees in New Jersey. The Dutch elm

111

disease, caused by a fungus, is now destroying many of our
beautiful elm trees. This fungus is spread by beetles. A few
years ago, as much as $50,000 a year was spent in New Jersey
to control this disease. Today, not much is being done about

N. J. Dept. of Agriculture

Canker stain destroys plane or sycamore trees. The infection was
started by wounds in the tree.

it in New Jersey. Unfortunately, the public does not seem to be interested in having money used for this purpose.

The spread of fungi can be slowed down by using sprays and by immediately cutting down burned, injured, or dis-

N. J. Dept. of Agriculture

Camden County trees destroyed by canker stain.

eased trees. Property owners with only a few trees can do this. It is more difficult to do on large wooded areas.

Trees weakened by fire also serve as breeding places for certain insects. Insects are our most abundant form of animal life. There are said to be over 10,000 species of insects in New Jersey. Many of these insects attack trees and shrubs.

Some insects attack the cones, seeds, and flowers of trees. These do not often kill the plant but slow down its repro-duction. Some insects suck the leaves and stems of plants.

113

The common ones are called scales and aphids. These weaken the tree or shrub. Others, like moths, sawflies, and beetles, eat leaves and the inner bark of the plant.

N. J. Dept. of Agriculture

Bark beetles make these burrows on elm trees.

The white-pine weevil is an important insect which destroys our white pine trees. Young trees are killed, and older trees are injured, spoiling their appearance and shape. The pine sawfly is another harmful insect. It attacks red pine and Scotch pine. The pine sawfly was first discovered in New Jersey near Somerville, in 1925. It came originally from Europe. Now it is found all over the state.

Scientists are always studying methods of controlling tree diseases and insect pests. If trees are properly maintained, they often have a better chance of fighting diseases and insects. We can all assist by preventing fires in wood lots and

N. J. Dept. of Agriculture

Tent caterpillar larvae make unsightly nests and destroy vegetation.

forests. If we have diseased trees on our property, we can cut them down and burn the diseased parts.

4. *Fires destroy organic matter in the soil.*

In an earlier chapter we learned about soils. We found that good soils contain much plant and animal life, mixed with the minerals. We learned that humus is an important part of the soil. A hot fire in a wooded area may destroy the organic matter and the humus. This will leave the topsoil in a poor condition. New plants will have difficulty growing in it. It takes many years for a good productive soil to form again after the soil has been badly burned.

5. *Fires may cause floods and increase erosion.*

We have already learned that organic matter in the soil holds back rain water. The organic matter acts like a sponge. When the sponge cover on a soil is destroyed, the run-off of rain water is increased. This not only wastes water, but may cause floods after heavy rains. The increased run-off may also cause more soil to be carried away. This increased erosion wastes soil and starts gullies, as we saw in the chapter on soil.

6. *Fires kill wildlife and destroy its food and shelter.*

Whenever there is a big fire, many animals lose their lives. Some try to outrun the fire and are trapped by it. Squirrels, deer, birds, and other animals are often burned alive. Birds also lose their nesting places. Other animals lose the food and shelter that they need and often die as a result. The fire kills trees, so that there is less shade than there formerly was. This lets sunlight into the woods and raises the temperature of streams, so that fish suffer. Fish cannot live in water that is too warm. Many fish also die from ashes and gases that get into the streams in which they live.

7. *Fires destroy beauty.*

A forest or wood lot fire leaves the landscape naked and unbeautiful. If you have ever seen a burned-over piece of woodland, I think you will agree that it looked ugly, barren, and dirty. A scar is left on the landscape and on your memory.

We have just seen that a carelessly started fire causes a "chain reaction." This means that one thing leads to another.

We have seen that a fire may cause animals to leave the region or be killed. Birds, moles, and shrews eat large numbers of insects. Moles and shrews are small animals living in the

N. J. Div. of Fish and Game

Scene in Burlington County after a forest fire

ground. If birds, moles, and shrews are killed or leave the region, insects will increase in number. These insects will do more damage to the remaining trees and shrubs. Floods may occur, and erosion will then be increased. Forest fires cause widespread damage. It is the responsibility of every citizen to do all he can to prevent forest fires. We do not want unnecessary waste of valuable natural resources.

117

Section 4. FOREST-FIRE CONTROL

The Coastal Plain area of New Jersey is one of the greatest fire hazard areas in the United States. Many people have summer homes in this area. The land is level and sandy. Winds sweep over it easily, without being stopped by hills, and dry out the ground. When a fire is started, the wind can fan the blaze dangerously. Also, the pine tree is the chief tree in this area, and pine trees burn easily. In the northern part of the state, conditions are different. Fires are not so common, and they do not burn as easily, in the wooded areas there.

The Forest Fire Section of the Bureau of Forests, Parks, and Historic Sites tries to protect our forests from fires. The Forest Fire Section is under the direction of a state fire warden. The fire warden has a deputy fire warden under him. The headquarters of the state fire warden is in Trenton.

The state is divided into three divisions for forest-fire fighting. Division A has its headquarters in Butler. This division has charge of the northwestern part of the state. Division B protects central New Jersey, and its headquarters is at Toms River. Division C has charge of the southern part of the state, south of the Mullica River. Its headquarters is at Mays Landing. A division warden is in charge of each division. Each division is divided into sections. There are 32 sections in the state. A section warden is in charge of each section. The sections are divided into districts. There are 372 districts. These districts are the local units for fire fighting.

A warden is in charge of each district. He and his crew are trained volunteers. They are on call for service at all times. As soon as a fire is reported to the district warden, he calls his crew by telephone, and they go to the scene of the fire. These men have a truck with tools. They use shovels, rakes, brooms, axes, and other hand tools. They also have

118

portable tanks. These contain water and are carried on the men's backs. The men spray the fire with the water from these tanks. If the fire is a very large one, the district warden will call for help from the section warden. The section war-

N. J. Forest Fire Service

Where water is available, a tanker truck like this can pump a stream over a mile from brook or pond.

den will send in larger tanker trucks. These trucks carry water which can be squirted on the fire. If the district warden asks him to, the division warden will send in more trucks and specially built plows. These plows make a furrow or trench in the sand around the fire, and this trench or furrow stops the fire from spreading on the ground. Tankers, plows, and men with hand tools put out most of the fires in New Jersey.

If the fire is a severe and large one, the state warden or his assistant may fly over it in an airplane. A map will be dropped from the plane showing the way the fire is moving. Directions

N. J. Forest Fire Service

Plowing a fire break. This type of plow is very useful in the southern half of the state where the soil is sandy.

can be given to the men on the ground telling them how best to fight the fire. In New Jersey, men are not dropped from planes or helicopters as they are in the western United States. We have a good road system which permits fire fighters to get close to the fire. This is not so in the West.

120

Fires are discovered and reported in either of two ways. People traveling through a wooded area often see the fire and telephone to a warden. Also, many fires are spotted by

Fire towers like this one are located all over the state.

the watchers in fire towers. There are twenty-two fire towers throughout the state. Men are usually in these towers for three months in the spring and one month in the fall. These are the times when most fires occur. If it is very dry, as it was in the summer of 1954, men are in the towers during the dry periods. The watchers in the towers are equipped with

121

radio and telephones. When a towerman sees smoke, he calls the nearest warden and reports the location of the fire. By looking through instruments, the man in the tower can locate the fire on a map. This location is accurately determined if two different towers report the fire.

N. J. Forest Fire Service

Shovels, brooms, and knapsack spray tanks are brought into action by a crew of forest-fire fighters.

Forest-fire fighters have to be very well trained. They must be stout-hearted men, who can keep calm and who are not easily frightened by fire. Also, they must be willing to work whenever called upon. They must have the respect of the men who are in their crew and working with them. Forest-fire fighting is a dangerous occupation, and not all men are qualified. There are in New Jersey over three thousand men who are enrolled as local forest-fire fighters. In an emergency, another three thousand men can be added to this staff. Enough hand tools and other equipment are stored in different places in the state to equip ten thousand men to fight fires.

The New Jersey Forest Fire Service is an outstanding organization. It has kept the size of forest and wood lot fires to a small area each year, even though the number of such fires is increasing. This is due to the efficiency of the fire fighters and their equipment. There is a radio voice communication system between sixty-five fire trucks and the section, division, and state headquarters. This makes possible speedy responses to fire alarms. Although this service is done efficiently, it does not take from each person the responsibility for preventing fires from starting.

Section 5. KINDS OF FIRES

1. *Ground fires.*

Ground fires are fires which burn down under the surface of the ground, in the duff or humus. Duff is the name given to the dried material just below the ground level in forests. Sometimes this is also called turf. After a long dry spell the dried roots may catch fire and burn slowly for a long time. A lighted cigarette carelessly tossed on the ground may start a fire of this nature. A ground fire destroys humus and plant food materials in the soil. It may do damage to the plants by killing the entire root system so that the plant will die.

Ground fires can be extinguished only by heavy rains which soak the ground thoroughly. Sometimes their advance is stopped by digging a trench or furrow around the fire area. The trench is dug into the mineral soil so the fuel is removed.

2. *Surface fires.*

Surface fires are fires which burn leaves and litter on the surface of the ground. If there are dry pine needles on the

123

ground, they may burn very rapidly. Other leaves may burn more slowly. A surface fire may deform or kill young seedlings. It burns the bases of older trees, causing wounds through which fungi and disease-producing bacteria may enter. Surface fires also destroy the duff and humus which are nature's forest fertilizer.

Surface fires are extinguished by the use of water or by beating or sanding. Beating is done with brooms, shovels, green branches, or burlap bags which have been moistened. Hitting the fire with these objects smothers it. Sanding means that the fire is smothered by throwing sand or soil on it. Sometimes a plow is used to dig a trench, to prevent this type of fire from spreading.

3. *Stand fires.*

Stand fires are fires which burn the lower growth of trees and brush. These fires also run over the ground and do the same sort of damage that the surface fires do. In addition, they often damage or destroy the bark on older trees. Most of the fires in New Jersey's woodlands are stand fires.

Stand fires are usually controlled by throwing sand or soil on them. If water is available, it also is used.

4. *Crown fires.*

Crown fires are those fires which burn in the tops of trees. They are very common in pine forests such as are found in southern New Jersey. If there is a strong wind, a crown fire will race through the forest very rapidly. Crown fires are exceedingly dangerous fires, killing all plant growth except the main trunks and large branches of old trees.

In order to control a crown fire, a "backfire" is usually started. A backfire is a new fire started by the fire fighters ahead of the main fire. It burns back slowly toward the main fire, using up the fuel, so that the main fire stops because of the lack of fuel. Only an experienced fire fighter should ever start a backfire, because there is great danger that this second fire may get out of control.

Shapes of Fires

Most forest fires burn in the shape of an oval or egg. The narrow end of the egg is the "head fire." This part travels before the wind and is the most destructive and rapidly moving part. The two sides of the oval or egg are the "side fires." The side fires burn less fiercely and less rapidly than the head fire. The large end of the egg is the "tail fire." This part of the fire burns back against the wind. It burns slowly and does not make a hot fire. A fire of the sort described may burn one mile in eight minutes, in a forward direction.

If there is no wind blowing, the fire may burn in the form of a circle instead of a long oval as described. Usually there is a breeze when there is a fire, so the common shape of the fire is the oval.

"Spot fires" are fires which start when sparks from the main fire jump out of the oval or circle. These may start another main fire at a distant point.

Section 6. RULES FOR FIRE PREVENTION

The State Fire Warden has prepared a list of rules for the prevention of forest fires. All of us should know these rules and try to follow them.

1. *Rules for smokers:*
   A. Break your match in two before throwing it away. If you do this, it will probably be cool and will not start a fire.

    B. Be certain that all cigarette, cigar, and pipe ashes are cold before they are thrown away. Scrape all organic matter away, and grind the cigarette or cigar remains into the mineral soil with your heel.

    C. Use the ash tray in your car, and never throw any lighted object from the car window.

    D. In windy or very dry weather, do not smoke at all in dry wooded areas.

2. *Rules for campers:*

    A. Do not build a fire near a wooded area without a permit from the local district fire warden.

    B. Read carefully all of the rules on the permit and follow them.

    C. Clear an area of at least ten feet around the fire.

    D. Never leave the fire unattended.

    E. Keep the camp fire as small as possible.

    F. Put the fire out when finished with it, using water if available.

    G. If water is not available, dig a hole around the fire and bury the ashes at least six inches under sand or dirt. Test the area with the palm of your hand. If it is too hot to touch, the fire is not out. Do not leave until the ground is cool enough to touch.

3. *Rules for brush burners:*

    A. Secure a permit from the local district fire warden.

    B. Read and follow all conditions and rules on the permit.

    C. Keep the piles of brush small, and add brush a little at a time as the fire burns down.

    D. Have men and fire-fighting equipment nearby to make certain that the fire does not get out of control.

    E. Do not burn brush on a dry or windy day.

F. Do not leave the fire unguarded for even a minute.

G. When burning is finished, dig a deep hole and bury all ashes and coals. These should be at least six inches under the ground. Cover the hole with soil and level it off even with the ground.

Remember that a written permit is necessary for building any fire within 200 feet of woodland in any town, borough, or township where there are fire wardens. The permit is secured from the local district fire warden. If there is one in your community, learn who he is. There is no charge for the permit. Remember that this law applies to privately owned land, as well as land owned by the state. Permits are not needed for fires built in tight containers.

Whenever you see a forest fire that has just started, go to the nearest telephone. Ask the operator to connect you with the local fire warden. Tell him exactly where the fire is. Do not try to put the fire out yourself. People with training and experience can put the fire out more easily than you can. Fires are dangerous things to work with.

SOME THINGS TO THINK ABOUT

1. What losses, other than the destruction of timber, are caused by wood lot and forest fires?

2. What punishment would you think best for a person who is caught setting a forest fire? Why?

3. Why are there more forest and wood lot fires in southern Jersey than in the northern part of the state?

4. What effect do forest fires have on wildlife?

5. Why do more forest fires occur in the spring than at any other season of the year?

6. How do many forest and wood lot fires affect the water resources of a region?

127

7. What precautions should be taken when building a camp fire? When leaving the camp site?

8. What is the difference between a surface fire and a crown fire?

9. How may forest fires affect you even though you may live in a city or town far from the fire?

10. What can each of the folowing do to help prevent forest fires?

    a. a teacher

    b. a newspaper editor

    c. a radio or television program director

SOME THINGS TO DO

1. Get acquainted with the nearest district fire warden, if you live where there is one. Ask him if he would come to your class or school, if the teacher is willing, to talk to the students.

2. Ask your teacher to secure from the State Fire Warden in Trenton a motion picture on fires in forests. Show this to the class.

3. Write an article for your school or town paper on the subject, "Protecting Our Forests and Wood Lots from Fire."

4. Make a poster telling some story about forest-fire prevention.

5. Make a chart showing some important rules for fire prevention.

6. Write a poem about forest fires.

7. Obtain a copy of the Forest Fire Laws for your school or class library. Write for it to the State Fire Warden, Trenton, New Jersey.

8. Read the fire laws, and try to remember the most important ones.

128

9. Make a scrapbook of newspaper clippings and pictures about forest fires.

10. Write an imaginary story about an animal caught in a forest fire.

SOME TERMS YOU NEED TO KNOW

Backfire—A fire started ahead of the fire to be put out, and directed back toward it.

Crown fire—A fire burning in the crowns or tops of trees.

Duff—The ground covering of decayed vegetable material in forests.

Fungi—Plants which do not have chlorophyll or green color, and which get their nourishment from the organic matter of other plants.

Ground fire—A fire which burns down under the surface of the ground.

Stand fire—A fire which burns the lower growth of shrubs and trees.

Surface fire—A fire burning materials on the surface of the earth.

Chapter Six

Some Animals of the Woods and Fields

Section 1. INTRODUCTION

The mammals and the birds which live in our woods and fields are very important natural resources. Many of them supply people with food. Hunting and trapping in New Jersey are big businesses, which benefit many people. The sale of ammunition, sportsmen's supplies, gasoline, and food for hunters provides work for many people. The recreational value for those who go out to hunt or merely to look at the mammals and the birds is very important.

Tourists and visitors to New Jersey often express surprise at the thought of our having wildlife in our state. Traveling along our main highways, these visitors see only large cities and industrial sites. Few of them get onto the roads in the rural counties. They fail, therefore, to see our beautiful forests and open fields, in which wildlife abounds. Of course, we do not have big game, such as is found in Wyoming or Montana. We have more hunters and fishermen per square mile of land, however, than any other state in the United States. The food value of the fish and game taken in New Jersey each year is at least two million dollars.

There was a time, a few years ago, when New Jersey's

mammals and birds were disappearing rapidly. It is because of the leadership of thoughtful conservationists that we now have so many animals. We have, in New Jersey, a Division of Fish and Game which is a part of the Department of Conservation and Economic Development. The wise leadership of the men in this Division has done much to preserve our wildlife. Of course, the cooperation of all the citizens of the state has been necessary too. Fifty years ago, there were no ring-necked pheasants in our woods. The ring-necked pheasant is a native of Asia which has been successfully introduced into New Jersey. In 1911, only 150 deer were legally killed in the state. Now we have an abundance of these two animals. This is the result of a wise conservation program.

We learned in an earlier chapter that New Jersey has a wide variety of land types and a fine climate. These provide ideal conditions for many kinds of animals, if man will do his share to help them survive.

There are some persons who believe that no one should be permitted to hunt and kill wildlife. This seems almost as silly as to say that we should never cut down a tree or use our soils or water. It is true that there are some animals, such as certain birds, that should not be killed. These animals help us more by being alive, as we shall see in later sections of the chapter. Other forms of wildlife must be killed, however, or they would seriously interfere with our activities, or they could crowd each other out. In some parts of New Jersey, for example, there are more deer and rabbits now than there should be. There is not enough food for all of them, and they turn to our crops for food. The rabbits damage our gardens, our trees, and our shrubs when they cannot get their food elsewhere. If we did not permit hunting, many wild animals would in time die of starvation and disease. There should be as many animals as existing food and shelter will support. We must realize that it is no more wrong to kill a deer than it is to kill a cow or sheep. If the surplus animals are killed we are benefiting the ones that remain. They are raised so that the people of the state may enjoy them. Of course, any animal that is killed should be killed in a humane manner. No good sportsman wants to see any animal suffer.

Our pleasure should not come from the killing, as such. We should get our pleasure in hunting from the sport which it gives us. Even though a sportsman may hunt all day without making a kill, he must remember that he has enjoyed a day in the open in good company. This pleasure in the out-of-doors should mean a great deal to all of us.

Some people do not like to hunt with a gun. For these people, a camera can be a splendid substitute. To "shoot" one of the animals discussed in this chapter with a camera is often more difficult than to shoot it with a gun. It is a real thrill to capture on film the picture of a deer, rabbit, or pheasant.

In this chapter, the animals are considered in two groups. First, we shall learn about a few of the important mammals. Then we shall learn about some of the birds of New Jersey. In the following chapter, you will read about some of the animals that live in the waters in and around the state.

Section 2. SOME IMPORTANT MAMMALS OF NEW JERSEY

We have used the word "mammals" several times already. The biologist calls an animal a mammal if it has hair on its body and is warm-blooded. Mammals all nurse their young with milk from glands in their bodies. Most of the animals that are mentioned in this chapter are either game animals or fur-bearing animals. Game animals are animals which are hunted for their meat or for sport. Fur-bearing animals are taken mostly for their furs. Sometimes animals serve both purposes.

Deer

To some people, the lord of the Jersey forest is the deer. About 1900, deer were almost eliminated from our woods.

N. J. Div. of Fish and Game

Deer at rest

This was because of over-hunting and the cutting of much of our woodland. Today, due to good management, there are many deer in our forests. During a hunting season of less than one full week, there are about 5,000 bucks, or male deer, killed each year. This number refers to deer that are legally killed. Unfortunately, many others are killed illegally. Several thousand are killed by motorists, also. The counties in which deer are most abundant are Burlington, Hunterdon,

133

Morris, and Sussex. Deer are found in every county except Hudson.

In New Jersey, a special bow-and-arrow season of three weeks is held before the shot-gun season for small game and deer. This is a real sport. About 15,000 licenses are issued each year for the use of bows and arrows in deer hunting. In 1954, 319 deer were reported killed by archers. Most of these were killed in Morris County.

Deer like to live in the pine woods in South Jersey. Many also live in the hilly portions of the northern part of the state. Deer feed on bushes and the lower branches of trees. Only occasionally do they graze, as cattle do. Deer must have wooded areas in which to browse.

The male deer is called a buck and the female is a doe. Young deer are called fawns. They are usually born in the spring. The bucks grow antlers, which fall off in the winter. New antlers grow each year. The male uses his antlers to fight other bucks. During growth, the horn is said to be "green." It is of no value as a weapon at this time. For this reason, "greenhorn" is the name given a person not capable of shifting for himself.

Rabbits

To bag a deer is the dream of many hunters. However, in New Jersey, the animal providing sport and food for more hunters than any other is the rabbit. This mammal is found in every county of the state. It multiplies rapidly. One pair may produce twenty or more young rabbits in a year. Hunters of all ages and degrees of skill enjoy rabbit hunting. Rabbits may be killed for about one month each fall.

Rabbits eat plants of all kinds, including the bark of young trees in winter. They are most active at night and usually

sleep all day. Rabbits, when too numerous, can be destructive to gardens and young trees. They are valuable to the
sportsman but are sometimes a pest to the farmer. It is often
a problem to keep both groups of people happy.

Dorothy M. Compton

Baby cottontail rabbits

Muskrats

Muskrats are most abundant in our marshlands on the
Coastal Plain and in the lower Delaware Valley. They live
in burrows along the edge of the water. Often they build
houses of marsh plants piled high above the water level.

Muskrats eat plants and small water animals, like mussels.

The muskrat is New Jersey's most valuable fur-bearing
animal. Muskrats are numerous and easily obtained. Well
over 250,000 are trapped in New Jersey each year. Most of
the pelts are made into ladies' fur coats.

135

Squirrels

Our state has several varieties of squirrels. The most common ones are the gray and the red varieties. These live in our woods and parks. Every city park of any size has gray squirrels in it.

Dorothy M. Compton

A young gray squirrel enjoying a picnic lunch

Squirrels eat nuts, seeds, and small fruits. They often hide their food and later locate it by their keen sense of smell. By this habit of burying food, squirrels help plant trees. Many oak and hickory trees grow from acorns or nuts buried by squirrels and forgotten by them. Unfortunately, the red squirrel will eat young birds. One may eat as many as 200 birds a season. This makes the red squirrel a nuisance, since most of the birds are of greater value than it is to man.

Large numbers of squirrels are killed each year in New Jersey and are used as food. Occasionally their pelts are sold.

Raccoons

All parts of our state have raccoons. The raccoon is hunted with hounds that are specially trained for this purpose. There

Dorothy M. Compton

Raccoon eating a crab which he caught in the Manasquan River

are several thousand "coon hunters" in the state. The coon is valued not only for his fur, but for his flesh, which many people like to eat.

Raccoons are found in wooded and well-watered areas. They eat insects, fish, frogs, crayfish, corn, and vegetables. The raccoon does not store his food. He does not hibernate and in good winter weather remains active. If water is available, a raccoon will usually dip his food in it before eating.

137

If caught when young, raccoons are easily tamed. They will follow their master even through the streets of a large city. Sometimes their dispositions get ugly when they get old. Raccoons kept as pets must be bought from a licensed breeder. It is necessary for any person to have a license to keep any game animal in captivity.

Baby raccoons are called cubs, and they are born in the spring. The den is usually in a hollow tree. It is illegal to take young raccoons from a nest.

Raccoons may sometimes take a farmer's corn, and they often take poultry. They are of some value to the farmer because of the insects which they eat. When too numerous, they do more harm than good. Their pelts are valuable, and many farm boys like to earn extra money by killing raccoons.

Beavers

The number of beavers in New Jersey has increased beyond the capacity of the land to support them. Beavers have, in some parts of the state, made dams. The water from these dams floods the farmer's land and destroys his crops. Some dams have caused roads and railroad beds to be flooded. In the right places, beaver dams conserve water. They create ponds where ducks, muskrat, and fish live, and are generally beneficial.

Beavers are protected by law, and there is no regular trapping season. When it seems desirable, the Division of Fish and Game may grant special permission to trappers to take beavers. In 1954, about one hundred trapping permits were authorized. This was done by public drawing. Each permit allowed the holder to take three beavers. In February of 1954, there were almost 200 beavers taken by holders of special permits. Trapping was not permitted in 1955.

The beaver pelt is valuable and is used to make fur coats.

Beavers build their houses in the water. Their den is a house built of twigs and mud. The house has an underground entrance. There is a large, airy room above water level. The dams, which the beavers make by felling trees, keep the water level at the right height for the house. The water all around the house protects the beaver from many natural enemies.

Plant foods are the only kind eaten by beavers. They are particularly fond of the bark of softwood trees. For a full meal, a beaver may eat three pounds of bark from a poplar tree. Beavers store their food underwater for winter use.

Miscellaneous

In addition to the game animals discussed in this section, there are a number of other kinds of animals in the state. Many of these are hunted and trapped in varying numbers. Some of these are the fox, the mink, the weasel, and the skunk. Certain other mammals are not classed as game animals, but are interesting to learn about. There are, for example, the moles, which get into our lawn and make burrows. There are flying squirrels, which have a loose flap of skin that acts as a parachute while the squirrel jumps from tree to tree. The chipmunk, which fills its pouches with food until it looks as though it has the mumps, is another common mammal. If you watch overhead in the early evening, you may see the only flying mammal. This is the bat, a mammal that flies like a bird.

These are a few of the many interesting mammals found in our state. Each one is interesting for a different reason. Some are beneficial to man, and others are harmful to his interests. It is important for us to know about their habits and life histories. By learning of their food habits and their relation to man, we can better learn to practice good conservation measures. We can interest our parents in the animal life of the state and help them to know how to vote intelligently on conservation matters. For some mammals, we can personally provide food and shelter. Some we can protect from their enemies. These are all good conservation practices.

Section 3.   OUR FRIENDS, THE BIRDS

Introduction

The term "birds" is, of course, familiar to all of us. Birds are two-legged animals whose bodies are covered with feathers. Like the mammals, they are warm-blooded. Birds hatch from eggs, which are laid by the female. There are over 250 species of birds in New Jersey.

Birds are one of our most important and valuable natural resources. They serve man in many ways. Many people feel that birds are the most beautiful and entertaining of all forms of wildlife. Observing birds in the fields and woods, where they live, can afford much pleasure. Many people enjoy studying the birds as a hobby. In order to understand the many problems of wildlife conservation, one should become acquainted with the birds in their natural environment.

What Birds Do for Man

Birds serve man's interests in many ways. Some of these ways are described in this section. Perhaps you can think of other ways in which birds assist man.

1. Birds feed on and destroy insects which are harmful to man or to his animals and crops. Insects probably kill more trees, for example, than do fire and disease combined.

Some birds, like the snipe, probe with their long bills into the soil to find insects. Others, like the killdeer, robin, and bluebird, catch grubs and insects near the surface of the ground. On trees, you will often see chickadees, woodpeckers,

Dorothy M. Compton

Young sparrow hawks. A teacher raised these birds by hand, after their nest was washed out of the eaves of a school building.

wrens, and other birds searching for insects on the bark or leaves. There are some birds, like the flycatchers, swallows, and swifts, which catch their insect food while they are flying. Thus we see that in all places there are birds adapted to feeding on insects.

141

2. Birds destroy mice and other rodents which spread disease and destroy crops.

Some of the birds helping man in this way are the hawks, owls, and shrikes. Most hawks and owls help man. There

Dorothy M. Compton

Tree sparrow at feeder

are a few, however, which are harmful to man's interest, and they have given their relatives a bad name. If one man, wearing a dark suit, commits a crime, we do not arrest and punish all men wearing dark suits. Neither should we kill

142

all hawks and owls, just because a few species do harm. We should learn to identify the harmful species and destroy them. The sharp-shinned hawk, Cooper's hawk, goshawk, and great horned owl are four species which do destroy poultry and game animals. If you live in the country, you should try to learn to distinguish these from the other, beneficial, hawks and owls which feed largely on harmful rodents.

3. Birds destroy many weed seeds by eating them.

This group of birds includes those with thick bills adapted for crushing seeds. Some of them are the sparrows, such as song sparrows, chipping sparrows, tree sparrows, and field sparrows. Others are the goldfinch, junco, indigo bunting, and lark.

The goldfinch has been selected as the state bird for New Jersey. It is a cheery sort of bird, usually found in small flocks. The bright yellow body, with black wings, tail, and crown, make the male very conspicuous.

4. Birds act as scavengers.

A scavenger is a sort of garbage collector. Birds in this group eat dead animals and other waste materials. Some common scavengers are the buzzard, the herring gull, and the crow.

5. Birds are a source of food for man. Birds which are hunted by man for food and sport are called game birds. A few of these will be discussed in some detail. These birds may be killed by licensed hunters.

Pheasants

The pheasant is the most popular game bird in the state. The ring-necked pheasant is a beautiful bird. It is a cross between the Mongolian and Chinese pheasant. It was successfully introduced into New Jersey about 1912. Today, through the efforts of the Division of Fish and Game, there

143

are thousands of these pheasants. Each year, many thousands are killed by hunters. This is an example of what can be done to increase a desirable species, if enough people are really interested.

N. J. Div. of Fish and Game

The ring-necked pheasant

The pheasant thrives best in the northern and central parts of the state. Through breeding with improved stock from England, the New Jersey variety has been developed. The English pheasants were originally introduced into England from China.

Each year, there are about 70,000 pheasants hatched at the State Game Farm at Rockport in Warren County and at Forked River in Ocean County. About 30,000 of these birds are given to boys and girls in 4-H Clubs and other youth groups to raise. The boys and girls take the birds when they are one or two days old. They keep them until they are

144

twelve weeks old. At this time, the birds are taken back by the Division of Fish and Game. The boys and girls receive $1.50 for each bird raised. These birds and others, raised at the farm at Rockport and at Forked River, are released into the parts of the state where they will live best.

Pheasants are large birds, the males or cocks weighing up to four pounds. They are the size of a chicken. Pheasants nest in grasses on the ground. They have one brood a year. The pheasants which are stocked help provide sport for hunters. However, the birds raised wild are still the most important source of birds in the state.

Pheasants eat a variety of animal and vegetable matter. They eat many insects as well as corn and other grain, weed seeds, and fruit.

Quail

The quail, or bobwhite, as it is known to some, is found all over the state. Many of us enjoy hearing its cheerful whistle in the fields in the spring and summer. It thrives best in the agricultural areas of South Jersey. The quail is a great friend to the farmer because of the large number of insects which it eats. Quail like beetles and grasshoppers. Quail also are heavy grain and weed-seed eaters and are usually found where cereal crops are grown.

Large numbers of quail are killed in our state each year. Quail will breed naturally in New Jersey, but, to add to the natural stock, the Division of Fish and Game breeds them at a quail farm. This farm is located at Van Hiseville. About 30,000 birds are hatched here each year. Like the pheasant, many of the quail are raised by boys and girls. For each of these birds, they receive $1.15 when the bird is mature. About 25,000 quail are released each year. Most of these are liberated in South Jersey, where there is better cover for quail than in North Jersey. The quail are released when they are fourteen weeks old or older. The birds are set free in the fall before frost when food is most abundant.

Quail are small birds weighing about a half of a pound.

Quail nest in depressions on the ground near open areas. A young quail can run as soon as it is hatched.

Woodcocks

The woodcock is a migratory bird. It does not stay in New Jersey all the time as do the pheasant and quail. Migratory birds are under the control of the United States Government. A special license is required to hunt woodcocks. This is in addition to the regular state license required for hunting other birds.

The woodcock is about one foot long and weighs about seven or eight ounces. The flesh is very tasty.

Woodcocks eat worms, beetles, grubs, and other insects.

Some woodcocks nest in New Jersey. They usually have four young. When migration starts, they usually fly at night, resting in moist, wooded areas during the day. One needs a dog to find them, and they have a very erratic flight which makes them hard to hit. The woodcock is considered a fine game bird.

Ruffed Grouse

The ruffed grouse is not as plentiful as other game birds in New Jersey. It is found chiefly in the hilly areas of the northern part of the state. Some grouse are found, though, in the pine areas of Burlington and Ocean Counties. In South Jersey this bird is often called a wood pheasant.

The ruffed grouse is larger than a quail and weighs about 15 to 25 ounces. It is about the size of a frying chicken. It eats buds of plants, fruits, acorns, and seeds.

When trying to attract a mate, the male grouse beats its wings. This makes a drumming noise familiar to many who live in rural areas.

This bird has excellent flesh and provides good sport for hunters. Many consider it our finest game bird.

Migratory Waterfowl

This is a large group of birds including primarily ducks and geese. They inhabit the waters and marshlands, particu-

N. J. Div. of Fish and Game

Ducks and muskrats thrive in this Salem County marsh.

larly along the Atlantic Coast and Delaware Bay. During migration these birds stop over in the salt and fresh-water marshes of our state, to feed and rest. Thousands of these birds stop along the Delaware River, and many get inland

147

SOME ANIMALS OF THE WOODS AND FIELDS

on lakes and swamps. Most of these birds nest in Canada or the northern United States. Because of this, the United States and Canada have a treaty to protect the migratory waterfowl. In addition to the laws of the United States, New Jersey laws also protect these birds. All hunters should be familiar with the game laws.

Bird books will help you identify the many different species of waterfowl. There are about 25 kinds of ducks alone, in New Jersey. Six species of rail and three species of geese are found here. These are only a few of the many waterfowl in our state. The Division of Fish and Game has done much to encourage waterfowl. It has created new breeding areas and has saved and improved marshes. These provide water and food that these birds need. Many thousands of hunters get recreation through harvesting the annual crop of waterfowl.

What Man Can Do for Birds

We have just read of five ways in which birds assist man to live better. Since the birds assist man, it seems fitting and wise for man to help the birds when he can. How can man help our feathered friends?

Birds, like all other forms of life, must have three primary things. These are food, water, and shelter. Anything man can do to fill any of these three needs for the birds will repay him many times over. The number of birds will increase as the food, water, and shelter are provided. It makes no difference whether man lives in the city or in the country. He can be of particular help to the song birds in both places. In the city, a property owner can plant shrubs around the yard. There are many shrubs which bear fruits and berries which birds like to eat. A few examples are sunflowers, crab apples, European cranberry, birch trees, and juniper trees.

To supplement the natural foods, man can put out additional foods. Birds like suet, peanut butter, bread crumbs, and meat scraps. Your school library may have booklets tell-

Dorothy M. Compton

White-breasted nuthatch at feeding station on tree

ing you how to set up a feeding station for birds. If it does not have these bulletins, ask your teacher to get them. They may be obtained from the Superintendent of Documents, United States Printing Office, Washington, D. C. These bulletins tell how to make food racks and food containers, besides describing the food materials.

Birds appreciate a bird bath with water in it all year. In

149

the winter it is necessary to see that the water does not freeze solid. Birds get in the habit of coming for water even in the winter. Sometimes a poultry heater can be used to keep the water free from ice. Of course, warm water can be put out each cold day.

Shelter can be provided for the birds by evergreens planted in the yard. Some birds will use nests and houses provided for them in the spring. Directions for building birdhouses can be obtained from booklets put out by the United States Government. Write to the Superintendent of Documents in Washington, D. C., for a list of these booklets. Even though houses are not built, you can assist the birds by putting out short pieces of string. Birds use string or pieces of cloth to build their own nests. Some mud in the yard will be appreciated and used by many birds. Robins almost always use mud in building their nests. The Division of Fish and Game has found that even large wild birds, like wood ducks, will use nest boxes made for them when hollow trees or other cavities are not available.

One must always remember that birds will not live near a place where there are cats or other animals that disturb them.

Section 4. ANIMAL RELATIONSHIPS

In this chapter the mammals and birds have been treated separately. In nature the separation does not exist. All forms of animal and plant life are closely related. What affects one form of animal may affect another in a way that is little expected. Illustrations of this close relationship are shown in the following incidents.

A farmer once had had many ducks on his marshland at one end of the farm. He complained to his friend, a biologist, that now he had no ducks. His friend was interested and studied the situation. After considerable investigation, the biologist gave his report to the farmer. He explained that the ducks had disappeared because the farmer had permitted boys to trap skunks. Skunks eat the eggs of snapping turtles, which live in ponds and marshes. When there were no skunks on the farm, the number of snapping turtles increased. The snapping turtles ate the young ducks. The older ducks would not live where they were disturbed and went elsewhere to live and breed.

This illustration is a little extreme, but from it we can see that it is difficult to know how one action will affect another situation. These things all require careful observation and study. Sometimes long experiments have to be carried on before the correct answer to a problem is found.

Here is another illustration of relationships which are very important to people in New Jersey. Our state's cranberry crop in 1954 was 16 barrels for each acre of land used. Massachusetts gets 27 barrels and Wisconsin 54 barrels per acre. Scientists wanted to know why New Jersey's crop was so much poorer than that of other states. Scientists from Rutgers University discovered that Jersey cranberry growers were using "prescribed burning" and other advanced forestry practices to reduce underbrush around bogs. Burning the brush near the bogs kills wild honeybees. Bees carry pollen, and a well-pollinated bog produces more cranberries. Experimental plots, where bees were placed near the bogs, produced 50 per cent more cranberries than were produced elsewhere in the state. Cranberry growers will now probably try not to destroy the places where wild bees live. Perhaps they will bring domesticated bees to their bogs to help increase the cranberry crop.

Section 5. THE ACTIVITIES OF THE DIVISION OF FISH AND GAME

Only intelligent leadership and an educated public make it possible for us to have so much wildlife in our state. Fortunately for those who love the out-of-doors, we have had a Division of Fish and Game which has provided leadership. Fortunately, also, the public has cooperated with the Division of Fish and Game.

Policies for the Division of Fish and Game are determined by a council composed of eleven members. Six are sportsmen, three are farmers, and two are commercial fishermen. This council appoints a director, who administers the Division under their general policies. In the Division of Fish and Game there are trained technicians, research workers, game wardens, and other fish and game specialists.

The Division of Fish and Game in New Jersey is different from most other state agencies. The state provides the money for the operation of most state agencies out of general taxes. This agency, however, is financed almost entirely from money raised by the sale of hunting and fishing licenses. The Division of Fish and Game receives no money from the taxpayer who is not a hunter or fisherman. The legislature does not appropriate general tax money for the work of the Division.

Some money to carry on the work of the Division of Fish and Game comes from the United States Government. This money is given to the states as a result of laws passed by Congress.

The Pittman-Robertson Wildlife Restoration Act provides for an 11 per cent tax on sporting arms and ammunition. This money is apportioned to the states on the basis of the sale of hunting and fishing licenses, and on the basis of the area of the state. For every dollar the state spends for approved purposes, the United States gives back seventy-five cents out of the sum allotted to that state. This money is used to help maintain and increase game flocks and herds. This is done by land purchase, improvement of breeding grounds, and research and other projects. The state authorities select, plan, and direct the program in each state, after approval by the United States Fish and Wildlife Service. New Jersey receives between $60,000 and $100,000 a year under the Act.

To interest boys and girls in the wildlife of our state is one of the objectives of the Division of Fish and Game. The Division has lecturers who will visit schools when invited to do so. These lecturers show pictures and bring specimens of living things to the schools. They also set up exhibits at fairs throughout the state. In this way, they present the story of wildlife conservation to all the public. They have a caravan which visits camps during the summer camping period. This is very popular with boys and girls.

The Division also acquires and administers Public Hunting and Fishing Grounds in several parts of the state. Today there are about 70,000 acres in these tracts. Many hunters and fisherman would not have a place to hunt or fish if it were not for these public areas. One very large area of this sort is at Tuckahoe, in Atlantic and Cape May Counties. Another is at Colliers Mills, near Lakehurst in Ocean County. There are some in Sussex, Cumberland, and other rural counties. In these areas, the Division of Fish and Game practices wildlife management. Through planting, cleaning, and other activities, they supply food and cover. In 1954, about 5,500 acres of scenic wooded area along the Delaware River Water Gap were purchased. This is another area which will be developed for the sportsmen of the state. It has over four and one-half miles of river front, which will provide a good place for fish-

153

ing. Many deer, squirrels, grouse, and pheasants live in the wooded parts of the tract.

The Division encourages farmers and other property owners to cooperate with it in planting trees and shrubs. These provide food and shelter for wildlife.

A staff of 41 wardens is employed by the Division of Fish and Game. These wardens are especially trained for their work. They advise people about the laws and educate them in the correct way to treat the out-of-doors. Unfortunately, many people have never learned how to behave in the woods and fields. If people cannot learn to respect the property rights of others and abide by rules they have to be punished. The rules and laws are designed to give everyone an equal opportunity to harvest our fish and game. Laws are made for the benefit of all, and unfortunately wardens do have to make arrests each year.

Another function of the Division of Fish and Game is to prevent wild animals from becoming a nuisance. Some animals are destructive to property when they are too numerous. Frequently, such animals as the fox, oppossum, squirrel, and hawk become too numerous in one locality. A man is then sent to capture or kill the animal which has become a pest. Sometimes such animals are caught and transferred to a part of the state where they are less numerous. Deer are the most serious property damagers among our wildlife. In many sections of the state, deer are a real nuisance to crops, gardens, and landscape plantings.

Section 6. GENERAL PROBLEMS OF WILDLIFE CONSERVATION

Two big problems in the conservation of wildlife have already been discussed more fully in other chapters. One is the problem of how to prevent forest and wood lot fires. This was discussed in the chapter entitled "Our Black Acres." Fires destroy food and cover for animals as well as killing the animals themselves.

The other problem is how to prevent pollution of streams. This was discussed in the chapter entitled "Water—The Lifeblood of New Jersey." Wildlife needs fresh water or it will die. Many of our streams no longer contain fish, which formerly were abundant in them. To solve these problems requires the cooperation of all citizens of our state.

All of us have a responsibility to do what we can to aid in the conservation of wildlife. It is the duty of people of all ages to abide by the laws and to report violators to the proper authorities. As we grow older, many of us will want to join conservation groups and sportsmen's clubs. Many of us have already developed an interest in the conservation program through scouting or 4-H Clubs. We can all feed wildlife in winter and provide shelter for birds. Perhaps you can think of other ways in which you can aid in the improvement of our wildlife.

SOME THINGS TO THINK ABOUT

1. What species of fur-bearing and game animals are found in your county? What other mammals are common in this area?

2. Are there as many fur-bearing mammals in your county now as there were ten years ago? Why?

3. For what reasons, other than the value of their fur, are mammals beneficial to man?

4. Why would it not be desirable, even if it were possible, to destroy all of the field mice, moles, etc.?

5. What are the basic needs for the existence of all wildlife?

6. How is wildlife conservation related to conservation of soil, water, and forests?

7. What are some factors which should determine whether hunting is allowed in any area of the state?

8. Why are birds considered to be among man's best friends?

9. What practices of man tend to reduce the bird population?

10. What natural forces and conditions tend to reduce the bird population?

11. How are some common birds adapted to particular types of activities?

12. Why are game laws and bag limits necessary ?

13. What changes in the present laws do you think might be desirable? Why?

14. Why are there restrictions on the types of firearms used?

SOME THINGS TO DO

1. Ask some hunters how hunting in your county now compares with hunting ten years ago. Find out if it is better or worse, and explain this condition.

2. Make a list of five principal factors that have caused the destruction of suitable habitats for wildlife in many parts of the state.

3. If possible, examine the pelts of some animals, observing the thickness, texture, and length of hair.

4. Look in the mud of a stream bank or in newly fallen snow for the tracks of some mammals. Make sketches of these tracks, and try to identify them.

5. Visit a store in the city, and ask the proprietor to show you the furs he sells and to tell you the names of the animals from which they were obtained.

6. Visit one of the state game farms, and learn about the problems of raising the animals there.

7. Find out what laws govern the hunting of the common animals of your county.

8. Obtain a copy of the game laws, and find out what the bag limit is for certain species of mammals of your county.

9. Establish feeding stations for birds near your school or home.

10. Start a collection of pictures of the animals mentioned in this chapter.

11. Suggest to your teacher that your class invite a speaker from the Division of Fish and Game to come to your school for an assembly program.

12. Go to the library and find out more about the life histories of some of the animals mentioned in this chapter.

13. Keep a record of the mammals and birds seen in your county.

14. Learn the songs of some of the common birds of your neighborhood.

15. Listen to records of bird songs and try to learn some.

16. Conduct a quiz program in your class, discussing the reasons for conservation laws.

SOME TERMS YOU NEED TO KNOW

Mammals—Animals which are warm-blooded, having hair on all or part of their bodies and nursing their young with milk.

Migratory—A term used to describe an animal which goes from one region to another to live.

Scavenger—An animal that eats wastes and refuse.

Species—A group of plants or animals which have in common one or more distinctive characteristics.

157

Chapter Seven

Some Animals That Live in Water

Section 1. INTRODUCTION

We have just learned in the last chapter about some important animals that live in our woods and fields. We saw that these are very valuable resources. There are also many animals that live in water and are of importance to man. These are less well known to many of us. Many of the animals that live in water provide recreation for thousands of people. These animals also often furnish us with food which is highly nutritious. The average fish, for example, contains at least five beneficial minerals and at least five vitamins. Many of these animals are a good source of protein, which is needed for building tissue in our bodies. In New Jersey, many persons are employed in industries associated with animals that live in the water.

First we shall learn about some fresh-water fishes. Other sections will tell us about the salt-water fishes and other interesting forms of animal life in the salt water.

Section 2. FRESH-WATER FISHES

Fish are cold-blooded vertebrates which usually have scales covering their bodies. The word "vertebrate" means an animal with a backbone, or vertebral column, like ourselves. The term "cold-blooded" means that the animal keeps about the same temperature as the surroundings in which it lives. Warm-blooded animals, like ourselves, have blood at a higher tem-

Warren E. Kruse, Trenton Times

Annual fishing contest for boys and girls, Trenton, New Jersey

perature than the air or water around them. Our own body temperature is always about 98.6 degrees Fahrenheit. Fish breathe by means of gills, and they live in water.

New Jersey has many species or kinds of fresh-water fishes. All of the largest ones provide excellent sport for the fisherman. We have over 800 lakes and over 100 streams and rivers in which these fish live. There are, in New Jersey, nearly 1,400 miles of streams with water cool enough for trout to live in during the early spring. Ninety per cent of the streams

159

of the state are open to the public for fishing. Fishing is a sport enjoyed by people of all ages.

Many farmers in New Jersey are building ponds on their farms. These ponds are being stocked with fish. The farmer often puts manure or artificial fertilizer in the pond. This makes very small plants grow well. These plants are eaten by water fleas and other small animals. Young sunfish and bass eat this small animal life. Large bass then eat the smaller fish. The large bass are, in turn, eaten by man. In this way, farmers can have plenty of fish at low cost. A well-stocked and well-managed farm pond should produce at least 200 pounds of edible fish each year. Some day, fish farming may be carried on in both fresh and salt water, more than it now is. The time will come when people all over the world will have enough food from the natural resources of the waters of the earth.

There are many times more fish in the waters of our state than there are birds in the sky. However, most of us do not know the fish as well as we do the birds. A few of our common fish are discussed in this section. Getting to know these fish and their habits could be an interesting hobby for some who are reading this book. Walking along a stream bank or around the shore of a pond can teach you much, if you are observing. Perhaps a pair of boots will help you to explore some of the more shallow waters without too much discomfort.

Boys who are fourteen years of age, or older, must have a license to catch the fish discussed here. Also, a separate, special license in the form of a trout stamp is required for trout fishing. The fees from the sale of fishing licenses are used by the Division of Fish and Game. The money is used to pay salaries, to aid research, and to pay for the management of ponds and lakes. Some of the money is used to operate the fish hatchery at Hackettstown.

Taxes collected under the Dingle-Johnson Act also provide money for improving fishing in the state. The full name

Francis Leigh

Trout fishing in the Whippany River at Morristown in Morris County

of this act is The Dingle-Johnson Federal Aid in Fish and Wildlife Restoration Act. This act provides for a 10 per cent tax on fishing tackle and equipment. The money is returned to the states on the basis of area and the number of fishing licenses sold. For every dollar that the state spends for approved purposes, the United States gives back to the state, out of the money allotted, seventy-five cents. The United States Fish and Wildlife Service approves the projects selected by the state on which the money is to be spent. In New Jersey, the money is used for several purposes. These include experimental management of lakes, surveys of ponds and lakes, and studies of the food preferences of fish. New Jersey receives about $40,000 a year from this source.

Rules and laws are necessary so that all the people have a fair chance to catch their share of fish. Some people are not always good sportsmen and want more than their share. These persons ignore bag limits and use improper methods to catch fish. Some catch fish during the closed seasons. One reason for having a closed season is to protect the fish when they are breeding. When some fish are breeding they will bite at almost anything. Nest-building fish, like bass and sunfish, will even bite at an empty hook dropped in the nest. Catching fish this way would be very unsportsmanlike. If fish are caught during spawning or breeding season, they will not have a chance to lay their eggs. This will reduce the number of fish during the next year. Every fisherman should be a good sportsman. He should know the laws and the reasons for the laws, and, of course, he should also obey the laws. A copy of the fish and game laws may be obtained, without charge, by writing to the Division of Fish and Game, Department of Conservation and Economic Development, Trenton, New Jersey.

Trout

Three species of trout are found in New Jersey. These are the brook trout, the brown trout, and the rainbow trout. All are found in streams in the northern part of the state. Trout breed as the temperature falls in the autumn. They usually lay their eggs when the temperature of the water reaches about 50 degrees. They prefer cold streams with quiet pools in

162

them. If the temperature of the water goes higher than about 75 degrees, the trout will weaken and die. That is why there are not many trout in southern New Jersey. The streams there are too warm.

Warren E. Kruse, Trenton Times

Three-pound brook trout caught in Mercer County

The brook trout is one of the best-known species. This is a beautiful fresh-water fish and is the only trout native to New Jersey. The largest brook trout ever caught in New Jersey weighed seven pounds, eight ounces. It was caught in

163

the Manasquan River in 1953. A brook trout has firm flesh and is a superior food. It provides much sport for the fisherman, being easily taken on artificial flies. In summer, a large part of its natural diet consists of insects which fall on the surface of the water.

The rainbow trout is another beautiful fish. It is usually bluish or olive green on top, with sides of silvery green. Its color varies considerably. A broad band of purplish red extends along the side from head to tail. The roof of its mouth has zigzag teeth which distinguish it from other species of trout. The original range of this fish was on the Pacific slope of the Sierra Mountains from California to Alaska. When hooked, it puts up a good fight, and it is a favorite fish with fly fishermen. The largest rainbow trout ever caught in New Jersey weighed five pounds, five ounces. It was caught in the Wanaque Reservoir in Passaic County.

The brown trout was brought here from Europe. It is usually dark brown on top, but, like the other trout, its color varies. The sides have red spots with light-colored rings around them. Brown trout prefer the larger streams of the state. The brown trout, like the rainbow trout, can live in warmer waters than the brook trout. The largest brown trout ever caught in New Jersey weighed ten pounds, twelve ounces. It was caught at New Wawayanda in Sussex County. All trout eat insects, worms, and snails.

Bass

Another abundant fresh-water fish in our state is the bass. There are two species of bass in New Jersey. One is called the large-mouthed bass and the other, the small-mouthed bass.

Bass like the warm, quiet water of ponds. Both species spawn, or lay their eggs, in the spring. Bass spawn when the water is about 62 degrees. Small-mouthed bass prefer to deposit the eggs in nests on the sandy or gravelly bottoms of ponds or rocky streams. The male makes the nest, which holds several thousand eggs. Large-mouthed bass lay their eggs in mud or silt in quiet water.

The large-mouthed bass has a long upper jaw extending back of the eye. The small-mouthed bass does not have this long jaw.

Both of these fish are good fighters when hooked. They will eat almost anything that moves but prefer insects, fish, crayfish, and frogs.

Both species of bass are warm-water fish. The small-mouthed bass likes colder water than the large-mouthed bass. Both will live in trout streams.

Sunfish

This is a name given to a family which includes many species. Most of the sunfish do not grow very large. They usually weigh less than one pound and are seldom over eight inches long. There are three varieties of sunfish which are most common in New Jersey. These are the long-eared sunfish, the bluegill sunfish, and the common sunfish, often called the pumpkin seed sunfish. The sunfish all live in warm waters of ponds or lakes.

Sunfish deposit their eggs in a circular nest on the bottom of the pond. The male guards the nest, and the young are protected by the male until they leave the nest. After that, the male will prey on the young sunfish. Sunfish are plucky fighters.

The sunfish eat insects, worms, crayfish, and small fish. Because of their fondness for mosquitoes they are good to have in a pond.

165

Long-eared Sunfish

This sunfish gets its name from its large ear flap, which has a narrow pale blue or red margin on it. It is one of the most brightly colored fishes found in fresh water.

Bluegill

The bluegill is a very well-known fish in New Jersey. It is the largest of the sunfish. Bluegills travel in schools and live in both streams and lakes. The flesh is firm and flaky, with a delicious flavor. The bluegill will eat almost anything it can get in its mouth.

Common Sunfish or Pumpkin Seed

This fish can be recognized by the red spot on its gill cover. It is a favorite fish with small boys.

Crappie

The crappie are sunfish which sportsmen value both for food and for their sporting qualities. Crappie reproduce very rapidly, and unless a pond is heavily fished it will become filled with stunted fish as a result of crowding. Crappie feed on insects and smaller fish.

Perch

There are two important species of perch in our state. These are the yellow perch and the white perch.

The yellow perch is a very sweet-tasting fish. Some say it is the best tasting of all fresh-water fish. The record for a yellow perch caught on a line is four pounds, three and one-half ounces. This fish was caught at Bordentown in 1865. In New Jersey, most perch do not exceed one pound in weight. The yellow perch lives in lakes and streams where there is little current. It usually travels in schools. This means that it travels in groups with other fish of the same species. The perch eats insects, worms, and smaller fish. The white perch is really a member of the bass family and is found in brackish or slightly salt water.

Walleyed Pike

The walleyed pike is sometimes called the pike perch. It is not related to the pike, however, being a close relative of the perch. This fish is a strong fighter and a good game fish. The world's record is twenty-two pounds and four ounces. The largest ever caught in New Jersey weighed almost thirteen pounds. This fish is dark olive green, with a yellowish appearance sometimes. It has a long, slender body like the pike. It gets its name from its very large eyes, which have a glassy cast. It breeds in the spring, and the parents do not protect either the young or the eggs. It eats small fish, worms, and insects. It likes warm water up to 70 degrees. This fish also travels in schools. In New Jersey, it is found chiefly in the Delaware River.

Catfish

"Catfish" is a term used to include a large number of species. They all have a large head, and the large mouth has whiskers or barbels on it. Their top fin has a very sharp spine on it. Because of this spine, these fish must be handled carefully. Catfish live in warm, muddy waters.

Most catfish hatch out their eggs in the spring, and the parents both guard the eggs and the young until they are an inch long. The catfish is a slow-moving, sluggish fish. In the winter, the catfish bury themselves in the mud. Catfish do not have scales as do most other fish.

Catfish eat almost any kind of food. Many people like the

167

taste of the meat of the catfish. Sportsmen do not consider it a game fish.

Chain Pickerel

The chain pickerel is one of the smaller members of the pike family. Chain pickerel may become over two feet long, but this is larger than the average in New Jersey. Until 1953, the world's record pickerel came from New Jersey waters. A Massachusetts fish caught in 1953 weighed nine pounds, three ounces. Fishermen have reported seeing pickerel in New Jersey that were three feet long. The largest on record in New Jersey was thirty inches long and weighed nine pounds. Most New Jersey fishermen fish for the chain pickerel. It lives in ponds and lakes all over the state.

THE STATE FISH HATCHERY

The fish hatchery at Hackettstown is one of the world's largest and best. It is operated by the Division of Fish and Game. Each year, over one million fish are raised at the hatchery. These are mostly trout and bass, with a few perch and sunfish. The fish are taken from the hatchery in trucks and put into the principal streams and lakes of the state. Only those waters which are open to the public are stocked with fish. Not enough trout breed in the streams to supply fish for all those who go fishing. The hatchery makes it possible for many more fish to be caught. The bass do reproduce well, but the stocking with fish from the hatchery increases the number of fish available.

Thousands of people visit this hatchery every year. It is a very interesting experience. Perhaps you can arrange for a visit there. It is open every day, and there is no charge for admission.

VALUES OF FISH TO MAN

In the preceding section, we have learned a little about some of our common fresh-water fish. Not only do they supply us with food, but they serve to control the growth of

N. J. Dept. of Conservation
and Economic Development

Transferring fish at State Fish Hatchery in Hackettstown, Warren County

small animals in the water. Fish, for example, eat many insects that are annoying to man. Sunfish and minnows do a splendid job in eating mosquitoes in the wriggler or larva stage, in both fresh and salt water. More important is the recreational value of fishing. Fishing helps people to relax and to take time to get outdoors and enjoy life. Many lasting friendships develop as a result of fishing with others.

169

Section 3. SALT-WATER FISHES

Salt-water fishes are valuable for the reasons that were given for the fresh-water fishes, and for one additional reason. Salt-water fishing in New Jersey constitutes a several-million-dollar industry. Many persons earn their living by working with fish caught in the ocean. For many, fishing is a sport, but for others it is a job.

New Jersey has about one hundred twenty-five miles of coastline on the Atlantic Ocean. It also has many miles of shore along Delaware Bay. Because of the large amount of coastline, we have many kinds of salt-water fish.

There are about sixteen thousand kinds of fish that live in salt water. Of these, about two hundred species are used by man. In New Jersey, there are eight species that are very valuable commercially. More than one million pounds of each of these eight fish are landed at New Jersey docks each year. Listed in the order of the number of pounds caught each year, they are the following species:

1. Menhaden
2. Porgy (Scup)
3. Sea Bass
4. Fluke
5. Whiting
6. Weakfish
7. Butterfish
8. Bluefish

Menhaden (Mossbunker, Bughead)

This fish is little known to most people in New Jersey. It is a member of the herring family. Although it is our most valuable commercial fish, it is not used as a food by man. It is not popular as a food, because it is very oily. Several hundred million pounds are caught each year in the coastal waters off Sandy Hook and Raritan Bay.

Menhaden are used for making fish oil and fish meal. The

oil is used in making soaps, varnish, paint, linoleum, and other products. The meal is used to make foods for poultry, cattle, and hogs. The wastes resulting from the manufacture of the oil and the meal are used to make fertilizers. This last value of the menhaden was known to the American Indians. They put a menhaden in each hill of corn that they planted. This acted as fertilizer. The name "menhaden" comes from the Narragansett Indian language and means "that which enriches the earth."

The menhaden average about one foot in length and weigh a little less than one pound on the average. They swim in closely packed schools and like the shallow water near bays and sounds. The heaviest catches are made in the spring.

The roe or eggs of the menhaden are often saved and frozen, salted, or canned.

Porgy (Scup)

The porgy, or scup as it is often called, is a small fish. Its greatest length is about eighteen inches. Those caught commercially weigh from three-quarters of a pound to one and one-half pounds. The porgies move northward, and toward shore, in the spring. They go southward, and toward deeper water, in the fall. Sportsmen fish for porgies along the Jersey shore in the summer. About 40 per cent of all fish caught by anglers in New Jersey are porgies. Those sold in the markets were probably caught by commercial fishermen. Porgies feed on worms, molluscs, and small crustacea, which they find on the bottom of the ocean.

Sea Bass

Sea bass are abundant off the Jersey coast from May until November. Sea bass are small fish, rarely weighing over four pounds. The largest one ever caught in New Jersey weighed six pounds. This fish has a white meat which makes very good eating. Because it swims over rocky bottoms, anglers do not like it. The tackle is easily cut on the rocks.

Fluke

The fluke is a variety of the flounder and is sometimes called the summer flounder. Fluke are flat fish with both eyes on the upper side of the body. They swim near the bottom of the ocean and feed on small fish, shrimps, crabs, and worms. A fluke may weigh up to fifteen pounds. The Women's World Record for this fish is thirteen pounds, eleven ounces, and it was made in 1953 at Long Branch, New Jersey. The largest fluke ever caught in Jersey waters weighed nineteen pounds, twelve ounces and was thirty-eight inches long. This was caught in 1953 at Cape May. Fluke are delicious to eat and are caught by anglers along the coast. Several million pounds are caught each year by commercial fishermen in Jersey waters.

Whiting (Silver Hake)

This fish is also called the northern kingfish. It is a good food fish, which spawns off the Jersey coast during the summer months. It is a fish which prefers sandy bottoms, where it catches smaller fish, crabs, worms, and squids. Whiting rarely weigh over three pounds. The whiting are usually cleaned and skinned, after which they are frozen and packaged for sale.

Weakfish (Sea Trout)

This fish is important both commercially and as an angler's fish. The name weakfish refers to the fact that the flesh is weak and easily torn by a hook. The weakfish usually travel in schools, although sometimes individuals will run up tidal waters. One of the largest weakfish ever taken was caught with a rod and reel in the Mullica River, in New Jersey, in 1944. It weighed seventeen and one-half pounds and was forty-six inches long.

Butterfish

Butterfish are small fish about eight or nine inches long and weighing up to one pound. They are becoming increasingly popular as a food fish. It is said that at one time dealers gave one away when a customer purchased other kinds of fish. Now over one million pounds of butterfish are caught in Jersey waters each year. Butterfish spawn during the summer months in bays and inshore waters.

Bluefish

Bluefish are excellent food fish with a very sweet flavor. Bluefish swim in schools and are very destructive to other fish. They seem to kill other fish just for the sake of killing. It is estimated that one bluefish eats twice its weight in a day, and kills ten or more fish daily. Bluefish are particularly fond of menhaden. Bluefish spawn in early summer off the shore.

Bluefish are excellent game fish. The largest ever caught in New Jersey waters weighed almost fifteen pounds and was slightly over three feet long. It was caught in 1950 at the Barnegat Jetties.

Shad

In addition to the eight species of fish which were discussed more fully in this section, there are about fifty others that are caught commercially. They are not caught in as large quantities, however. One species which used to be very abundant in New Jersey is the shad. Shad are considered a delicacy by many people. The roe, or eggs, are especially prized. Early colonists used to catch shad in nets as the shad migrated up rivers to spawn. Shad spawn in the early spring. The colonists caught so many shad that a wagonload was sold for one dollar. The shad were used as a fertilizer. Today shad are very scarce in our rivers and bays. This scarcity is due to overfishing and to pollution of the waters. Pollution is very bad in the Delaware River, and there are not many shad caught in the Delaware. Some are still caught in the Hudson River, because the water is freer from pollution. The shad are an example of what happens to our resources when they are badly managed. If good conservation measures are practiced and our rivers are free from pollution, shad may come into the rivers again.

METHODS OF CATCHING SALT-WATER FISH

Salt-water fish are caught in several ways. They are caught both by sportsmen and by commercial fishermen. The most important methods are described here.

FISH POUNDS

Many fish are caught commercially in fish pound nets. These are big nets fastened to stakes in the water offshore. Poles support a long net called a leader. As the fish swim by, they hit the leader, and it guides them into a funnel-shaped opening in the larger net which is a part of the pound. Each day, the fishermen come out and haul the nets into their boats to collect the fish trapped in them. These fishing boats are busy all year. Weakfish and bluefish are examples of fish caught in fish pound nets.

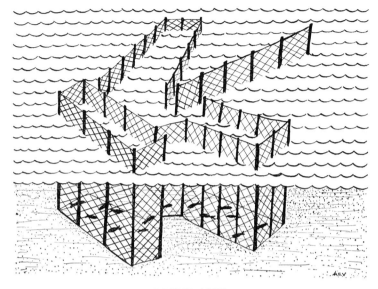

POUND NETS

OTTER OR BEAM TRAWLS

Another method used to catch salt-water fish is the otter or beam trawl. An otter or beam trawl is a large net, wide at the top and narrowing to a point at the bottom. It is shaped something like an ice-cream cone. The trawl is put in the water from a fishing boat. Machines, called winches, are used to raise and lower the trawl. The fishing boats cruise a couple of miles offshore. Most porgies and whiting are caught by this method.

PURSE SEINES

A third way of catching salt-water fish commercially is by the use of a purse seine. A purse seine is a big net. It is carried into the water by men in two small boats. These boats are put off the large fishing boat, when the fish are to be caught. A man, called a striker, is put off in a third small

175

OTTER TRAWL

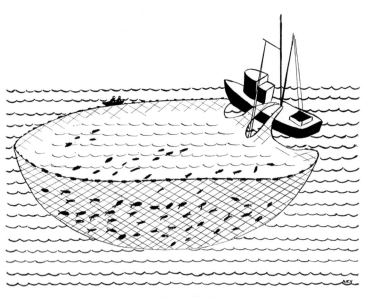

PURSE SEINE

boat. The striker tries to keep his boat over the spot where the school of fish was located. The men in the other two boats take the large net and let it out into the water, circling around the striker in his boat. The purse seine may be over

N. J. Div. of Fish and Game

Surf fisherman carrying a striped bass

a thousand feet long. It goes into the water to a depth of fifty or more feet. When the men think that they have the fish encircled, they pull a rope which is on the bottom of the seine. This rope tightens the bottom of the seine, like a purse, and the fish are trapped. The net, or seine, is then pulled up onto the larger boat. Menhaden and bluefish are caught in this manner. A good catch of menhaden will be about 100,000 fish in one seine.

177

Formerly, the captain of a fishing boat would order the nets or seines put out whenever he guessed that fish might be near his boat. Today, most fishing vessels are equipped with

Lewis D. Crowell

Surf fishing along miles of ocean front at Island Beach, Ocean County

an instrument called an echo sounder. This instrument, similar to radar, records the presence of a school of fish on a screen.

FISHING BY SPORTSMEN

Many salt-water fish are caught in New Jersey by sportsmen who enjoy surf fishing. Surf fishing is very popular all along the coast. The men stand on the beach and cast into the surf. Surf fishermen catch such fish as striped bass, weakfish, flounder, fluke, and bluefish.

Many other fishermen enjoy fishing from boats. Boats

leave many ports in New Jersey to take fishermen out to sea for line fishing. Tuna, weakfish, and bluefish are just a few of the species caught in this manner. Many fishermen fish from boats in Delaware Bay and other bays along the coast. They catch weakfish, bluefish, croakers, and many other

N. J. Div. of Fish and Game

Landing a tuna

species. The world record for pollock was made by a New Jersey fisherman at Belmar in 1953. The fish weighed over thirty-six pounds.

Fishing by sportsmen is important not only for its recreational value, but for the money and business it brings to hotel owners and businessmen. Salt-water fishes are a valuable natural resource in our state.

Individuals do not need a license to fish in salt water if they use a line. If a net or seine is used, a license is required.

Section 4. CRUSTACEA

Crustacea are animals that have their skeleton on the outside of their body. They have a body which is divided into three parts. Most crustacea live in water and breathe by means of gills. They all have a number of jointed feet.

There are two crustacea that are of considerable economic importance in New Jersey. These are the lobster and the crab. Both are used as food for human beings. Farther south, the shrimp is an important crustacean. In Jersey, the shrimp are small and used only for bait. In southern waters, they grow to be six inches in length. Southern shrimp are the ones sold in our markets.

Blue Crabs

There are several species of crabs, but the most important one in our state is the blue crab. This crab gets its name from the blue-green color of the top shell. The bottom part of the crab is white. The claw is blue.

Blue crabs, like most other crabs, live in shallow water. They prefer the muddy bottoms near river mouths. Here they find abundant vegetation in which to hide. The young crabs must live in rather salty water for the first two weeks of their lives. Later they can live in less salty water. The female crab carries a large mass of eggs, known as the "sponge," attached to her tail or abdomen. When it is time for the eggs to hatch, the female goes to deeper and saltier water. The eggs hatch in about fifteen days. This takes place in the summer. It is illegal to take and keep female crabs with eggs or spawn on them. It is also illegal to possess crabs from which the egg pouch has been removed.

Crabs have ten jointed legs. The first pair is usually enlarged, with a claw. Crabs can walk with these legs, but they also swim, going either backwards or sidewards. When they walk, they usually walk sidewards.

As the crab grows in size, it sheds its shell. This is called molting. A crab molts about fifteen times before it is fully grown. Crabs are mature, or fully grown, when they are twelve to fourteen months old. This is during the second summer of their life. The new shell is already growing under the old one. When the shell is shed, or molted, the new shell is soft for several days. When a crab is shedding, it is called a "shedder" or a "peeler." After the old shell is shed, and while the new one is still soft, the crab is called a "soft-shell crab." Many persons like to eat soft-shell crabs. The hard-shell crab is commonly cooked and eaten also. Only the meat of the hard-shell crab is eaten, whereas the entire body of the soft-shell crab is eaten.

Crabs are caught either in nets or on lines baited with dead animal matter. Sometimes crabs are dredged out of the mud by dredges on boats. A dredge is a big scoop. Crabs are sold either fresh, frozen, or canned. A barrel of crabs yields about twenty pounds of meat. If crabs are dredged, a license is required. Crabs may be caught by means of a handline, a rod and line, or a dip net, without a license. Lines must not have more than ten baits on them, however. The law requires that hard crabs be kept only if they are at least four inches across the shell. Soft crabs must be at least three and one-half inches across the back. Peelers must be at least three inches across the back.

Lobsters

Lobsters are very large crustaceans. They may grow to be several feet long and weigh up to thirty-five pounds. However, most lobsters caught in New Jersey waters are smaller than this. One of the largest lobsters ever caught off the Jersey coast was four feet long and weighed thirty-four pounds. Lobsters are dark green above, with darker spots. Underneath, they are yellowish. Like crabs, they have ten legs. The first pair of legs form large claws which act as pincers.

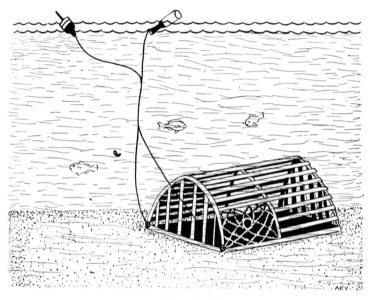

LOBSTER TRAP

Lobsters live on the ocean bottom in shallow water in summer and go to deeper water in fall. Lobsters may travel several miles a day. They are good scavengers, eating dead animal matter. Although they eat dead matter, they prefer live fish, molluscs, and other smaller crustacea.

Many people consider lobsters to be a delicacy. They can be broiled, boiled, baked or steamed.

Lobsters are caught in baited traps which are called "pots." In New Jersey, menhaden are used as bait. The lobster smells the bait and enters the trap. Each lobster trap or pot is fastened to a wooden float or buoy which floats on the surface. Each float is marked, so that the owner can identify his pot. Every few days, the lobsterman comes out in his boat and pulls up his pot to remove the lobsters. New Jersey law permits lobsters to be kept if they measure three and one-eighth inches from the rear end of the eye socket to the rear end of the body shell. No lobster may be kept if it has egg masses attached to it. This is a necessary conservation measure.

Lobsters molt, or cast off their shells, just as crabs do. Until lobsters are one year old, they molt several times. After that, they molt only once every two years. Lobsters often lose their claws in fights, but they can grow new ones quite easily. They can even grow new legs and eyes.

The female lobster carries the eggs attached to her tail for ten or eleven months. After hatching, the baby lobsters drift in the sea for from two to six weeks. Many are eaten by fish during this period. After molting three times, the young lobsters look like adults. They then go to the bottom of the ocean, where they spend the remainder of their lives.

Horseshoe Crabs (Horsefoot Crabs, King Crabs)

This animal is not really a crab nor is it a crustacean. Scientists say that it is related to the spider. However, since it is called a crab, and because many people think of it as a crab, it is included here.

The horseshoe crab may reach a length of two feet from its head to the tip of its long, spiny tail. It lives to be ten or more years old and molts or sheds its skin as many as sixteen times. It is shaped like a horse's foot. The horseshoe crab prefers the muddy bottoms of bays, where the water is not too salty. Here it feeds on clams and worms. The eggs of the

183

horseshoe crab are laid in the sands of beaches at the water's edge. The female scoops out the shallow nests in which she deposits her eggs. The young horseshoe crabs remain buried in the mud in the winter. Older horseshoe crabs swim to deeper water for the winter.

Large numbers of horseshoe crabs are caught in traps along the shores of Delaware Bay. Some are made into fertilizer. Others are cut up for lobster and eel bait. Some are used as food for chickens and hogs. The American Indians used to eat these animals. Often they used the sharp, pointed tail to make tips for their fish spears.

Section 5. MOLLUSCS

Molluscs are animals with soft, fleshy bodies. The soft body is usually encased in a hard shell made of lime. Molluscs do not have true legs. Some have a part called a foot. Other species, such as the squid, have long arms or tentacles. Molluscs are often called shellfish. They are not true fish, however.

The most valuable mollusc in New Jersey is the oyster. Clams, scallops, and squids are other molluscs that are of some commercial value in this state.

Oysters

The oyster industry in this state is now valued at about two and one-half million dollars annually. Over eight million oysters are sold here each year. The Maurice River Cove is one of the largest oyster-producing areas in the world. It is in South Jersey on Delaware Bay. Find it on a map of the state. Here there are about 33,000 acres of leased oyster grounds. There are also about 20,000 acres of state-owned natural beds which are open to the public. About 200 boats

operating out of this area are a part of the fleet which belongs to the oyster industry in New Jersey.

In New Jersey, the Division of Shellfisheries controls publicly owned oyster beds. The Council of this Division may
give permission to remove oysters from the beds. This is

Thurlow Nelson

Oyster boats at Bivalve

done in May and June. In New Jersey, areas open to the
public are known as "beds." Areas leased by individuals are
known as "grounds." Oyster grounds may be leased from the
state for $1.50 per acre, per year.

All of you have probably seen oysters, although many of
you have seen them only after they have been removed from
the shell. Oysters have a thick, hard shell on both top and
bottom. These are about four or five inches long. These shells
protect the body of the oyster.

A large female oyster produces over 100 million eggs. These are released from her body during June, July, and August. Five hundred of these eggs, laid side by side, would extend only one inch. Within twenty-four to thirty-six hours after the eggs are discharged into the water, a complete little animal is formed. This is called the "larva." The young larva is able to swim actively. The shell first appears on the oyster larva when it is about twenty-four hours old. The young larva swims about in the water for two weeks. Then it attaches itself to old shells, or other objects, in the water on the bottom of the bay. Now the young oyster is called a "spat." The spat can be just seen with the unaided eye. The old shells to which the spats are attached were put into the waters of the bay by the oyster grower or farmer. He did this in July, and the place where the shells were dumped is called an "oyster bed."

The oyster farmer takes the young oysters, now called "seed oysters," from the beds when they are about ten months old and puts them in his own private grounds. This is called "planting." Oysters grow in these grounds for from two to five years. At the end of this time, the oysters are about five inches long and are ready for the market. They are brought to the surface either by long tongs or by dredges, put down from boats. On the boats, the oysters are sorted out. The small ones and the empty shells are returned to the water.

Delaware Bay oysters are in great demand. They have a very fine flavor and are shipped all over the United States and Canada. Most of them are removed from their shells and shipped in ice-packed barrels.

The idea of growing oysters in grounds such as have been described came about by accident. About one hundred years ago, oystermen would take their oysters from the bay and carry them by boat to New York and Philadelphia. Sometimes, when the market was oversupplied, they had to bring their oysters home again. They took their cargo home and dumped it near their own docks. Later they found that these oysters had grown considerably. This made some of them decide to take oysters from the shallow waters of the bay,

Oyster boat at sea

where they usually lived, and to plant them in the salty, deeper waters of the bays. Here they grew better than before.

Oysters have many enemies. Fish, mussels, crabs, and other animals eat young oysters. There is a species of snail, called an oyster drill, which bores holes in the oyster shells, killing the oyster. In cooler waters, north of New Jersey, the starfish destroys many oysters. Starfish are not abundant in New Jersey waters. Storms and hurricanes damage many oyster

187

beds. By the end of the growing season, only one or two oysters are left of the millions of eggs shed by the female. Oysters grow best in pure water. If the water is polluted, it may affect the oyster. Oysters were once common in Raritan Bay, but pollution has destroyed these natural beds. Even though pollution may not kill the oyster itself, it may cause illness in those who eat it, if the oyster is eaten raw. This is a problem of conservation that affects all of us.

A license from the state is required to take oysters from any natural oyster beds in the waters of New Jersey.

Clams

Next in value, after the oysters, are the clams. Several varieties of clams are found in New Jersey waters. Three are commercially valuable. These are the hard clams, surf clams, and soft clams. New Jersey is one of the five leading producers of clams in the United States.

Clams, like oysters and scallops, are sometimes called "bivalves." This refers to the two shells that these animals have. Like the oysters, the clams have a soft body enclosed in the protective shells. In New Jersey there is a town called Bivalve. Find it on a map.

The hard-shell clam is the clam that is of greatest commercial value in our state. It is sometimes called "quahog." This is an Indian name. The American Indians were very fond of clams for food. They also took the shells of some clams and ground them into small beads. The quahog has a colored part inside the shell. This colored part made dark beads which were valued twice as highly as white beads. These beads were called wampum and were used as money by the Indians.

Because this species of clam has a small neck, or siphon, it is often called the littleneck clam. This neck or siphon is used by the clam to get food from the water. The hard-shell clam lives in sand-mud flats where the water is deeper than that preferred by other clams.

The soft-shell clam has a thinner shell than the hard-shell clam. It also lives in mud flats along the coast, usually in the zone between high and low tide. The soft-shell clam is about three inches long. Its neck or siphon may be longer than the shell itself. When this clam is disturbed in the mud, it shoots a stream of water into the air. Soft-shell clams are usually dug with a hoe or spading fork.

The surf clam, or sea clam, is very common along our beaches. It may be six or seven inches in length. This clam is used as food and also as bait. It lives in the sand from low-water mark offshore to depths of 100 feet or more in the ocean. Like the other clams, it is either dredged or dug out of the sand and mud with hoes or tongs. One of the chief dredging grounds is near Fifteen Fathom Light, off Cape May.

A license is required for the taking of clams from any natural clam grounds in the waters of New Jersey.

Many of our clam beds have become polluted by sewage.

Scallops

Next to the oyster and clam in importance comes the scallop. Our scallop of commerce is the giant sea scallop. It has a smooth shell about the size of a saucer. Most bivalves do not move fast, but the scallop does. By flapping its shells, it may move through the water several feet at a time. This is a natural form of jet propulsion.

The scallops are dredged like clams. The central muscle is cut out immediately after capture and is the only part which is eaten.

189

Squids

Although some people like them, squids are not commonly sold in New Jersey for human consumption. They are sold in a few of our local markets, however. Squids are nutritious and have good flavor. They are of considerable importance because of their use as bait for codfish and other salt-water fish. Sometimes squids are used as a fertilizer for soils.

Squids differ from the other molluscs discussed in this chapter because they lack the external shell. A squid has a body about eight inches in length, shaped something like a submarine. The ten arms are set in a circle around the mouth. The body is dark grey, with reddish spots. Squids can quickly change their color, however. The squid has two human-like eyes which are without eyelids. The giant squid, which lives in other parts of the world, grows to be as much as 50 feet long including the arms.

Squids live in deep water off the coast. When enemies disturb a squid, it discharges a black fluid. This fluid discolors the water so that the squid can escape. Squids are caught with pound nets, otter trawls, and seines.

NEW JERSEY DIVISION OF SHELLFISHERIES

In New Jersey there is a Division of Shellfisheries within the Department of Conservation and Economic Development. This Division consists of a council, a director, and persons employed by them. The Council has control of the shellfish industries. There are nine persons on the Council, not more than four of whom may be of the same political party. All members must be actually engaged in the shellfish industry. They may be planters, shippers, or owners or leasers of land on which shellfish are produced. The law requires that the members of the Council be from certain counties. There are three from Cumberland County and one each from Cape May, Atlantic, Burlington, Ocean, and Monmouth Counties. These members are appointed by the Governor, with the advice and consent of the Senate. They are appointed for a term of four years.

The Council of Shellfisheries makes rules that are necessary for the preservation and improvement of the shellfish industry. A license from the Council is necessary before anyone can take oysters or clams from natural beds. This license is issued for one year. The Council leases lands of the state, under tidal waters, for the planting and cultivating of oysters. It also regulates the use of boats in the natural beds, so as to prevent damage to the oysters.

The season during which oysters may be taken from the natural seed beds is also determined by this Council. The Council makes regulations regarding the number and the sizes of dredges used to remove shellfish. The minimum size of hard clams that can be kept is regulated by the Council of Shellfisheries. It makes and enforces regulations as to the number of shells which must be returned to the breeding beds.

It can be seen that the scope of this Council is very broad. It is doing everything it can to provide shellfish for all, both now and in future generations.

SOME THINGS TO THINK ABOUT

1. How is stream improvement for fish life related to forestry, soil conservation, and water conservation?

2. What is meant by the term "balanced water life"?

3. What, besides man, are some enemies of fish and marine life?

4. Why are there laws prohibiting the keeping of crabs and lobsters with egg masses on them?

5. Why is it necessary to have laws regulating the catching of animals that live in the sea?

6. Why are trout not found in South Jersey streams?

7. When fish lay thousands of eggs, why is it necessary to have fish hatcheries in New Jersey?

8. Why are shad not as common in our streams today as they once were? What can be done to increase their numbers?

9. Why are soft-shell crabs more expensive than hard-shell crabs in the restaurants?

10. How does pollution of streams affect the oyster industry?

SOME THINGS TO DO

1. Visit a fish market in your town, and ask the clerk to show you the sea foods which he sells. Name the fish and other animals, and tell where they came from, if you can.

2. Visit the fish hatchery at Hackettstown, and learn about how fish are raised there.

3. Examine nearby streams for evidences of pollution, soil erosion, or other conditions that might affect the fish.

4. Find out something about the laws governing fishing in the state.

5. Find out in biology books or an encyclopedia more about the life histories of some of the animals discussed in this chapter.

6. Bring one of the animals described in this chapter to your class, and show your classmates some interesting things about it.

7. Talk to fishermen in your area, and find out from them what fish they catch and how they catch them. What bait do they use?

8. Visit a store selling fishing tackle and supplies, and ask to see the different types.

9. At a sea-food store, buy and have opened for you an oyster or clam, so that you can study its body.

10. Visit some of the places where sea food is produced in New Jersey.

11. Conduct a quiz program in your class discussing the fish and shellfish conservation laws.

SOME TERMS YOU NEED TO KNOW

Abdomen—Part of an animal's body. In crustacea, it is the last section.

Cold-blooded animals—Animals whose blood changes to keep about the same temperature as the surroundings of the animal.

Crustacea—A group of animals, like the crab and lobster, which have a crusty covering of lime around their bodies.

Molluscs—A group of animals with soft bodies protected, in most cases, by a shell of lime. Examples are the oyster, clam, and snail.

Otter trawl—A large, bag-like net which is towed by a boat to trap fish or other sea life.

Pound net—A fish trap made of a net or nets supported to form an enclosure with a narrow entrance.

Purse seine—A large net, one edge of which is provided with sinkers and the other with floats.

Spawn—To produce or deposit eggs. The eggs of fishes, oysters, and other animals which live in water and lay many small eggs.

Vertebrates—A division or group of animals having a backbone such as is in our bodies.

Chapter Eight

Our Buried Treasure

Section 1. INTRODUCTION

Compared with many other states, New Jersey does not rank high in the possession of "buried treasure." However, in relation to its size, it is quite rich in rock and mineral resources. These resources are what is meant by the term "buried treasure."

To the geologist, the word "rock" means any non-living material which covers a large part of the earth's surface. This definition might include loose sand, or even ice. Rocks are usually made up of minerals. Minerals are inorganic substances with definite characteristics and properties. Minerals are always chemically the same. Rocks, on the other hand, differ greatly in their composition. Even though two rocks may be called by the same name, they may vary a great deal in the amounts of minerals composing them.

Early in the history of our state, people sought minerals in New Jersey. Remains of old iron and copper mines are found in several places in the state. Underneath the campus of Rutgers University there are the remains of an old copper mine.

In any one year, between 50 and 60 million dollars' worth of minerals and rocks are sold in New Jersey. Mineral resources are what scientists call "non-renewable resources." Unlike forests, for example, minerals and rocks cannot be replaced. When they are used up, there will not be new ones formed during our lifetime. It takes millions of years for nature to create rocks and minerals. Because of this, and because of the expense involved in removing them from the earth, man has been careful about their use. There has been little waste in mining operations in New Jersey.

Section 2. SOME COMMON ROCKS AND MINERALS AND THEIR USES

Zinc

Probably the best-known minerals of New Jersey are the ores of zinc. These are found in Sussex County, at Ogdensburg and Franklin. These zinc ores are world famous, because they are so rare and of such high quality. The Franklin Mine

Newark News

View of the Franklin Mine

closed in 1954, because most of the ores were exhausted. At Ogdensburg, zinc ores are still mined. Many rare minerals are found associated with the zinc ores. An entire book has been written about the interesting minerals of this region.

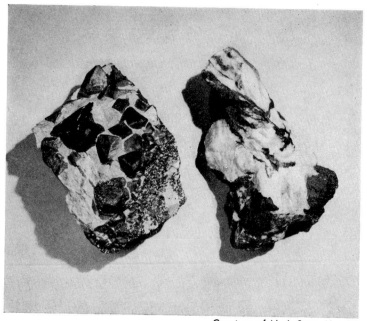

Courtesy of N. J. State Museum

Franklinite and zincite are two of New Jersey's valuable ores of zinc.

These minerals are very colorful and beautiful. Many of them glow with lovely colors under ultraviolet light. The zinc ores occur in beds of limestone. This particular limestone is called Franklin limestone.

Zinc is a very useful mineral. Galvanized iron is iron that has been coated with zinc to make it rust-proof. Zinc is also used in the manufacture of many articles, such as paint, paper, pottery, and rubber products.

196

Iron

The mining of iron has been carried on in New Jersey since colonial days. The Washington Mine, at Oxford, Warren County, has been operated almost continually since before the Revolutionary War. At Mine Hill, near Dover in Morris County, there is the Scrub Oak Mine. In 1954, this mine employed almost 500 men. Waste from the Scrub Oak Mine was used as fill for constructing parts of the famous New Jersey Turnpike. The newest iron mine is the Mt. Hope Mine, near Dover. This mine has a vertical shaft 2,700 feet deep.

The iron mines of New Jersey are not as large as those in Minnesota and other midwestern states. However, they are able to compete with them for two reasons. One reason is that New Jersey mines have a high-quality ore. The second reason is that the mines are near furnaces where the ore is converted into iron.

There are several kinds of iron ore. In North Jersey, the iron ore is a type called magnetite. On the Coastal Plain, there were formerly several places where iron was produced from an ore called limonite. This is the "bog iron" found in bogs and swamps. This ore is no longer used in New Jersey.

Clay

Clay is a very fine-grained substance, formed by the decay of certain rocks and minerals. When wet, clay is easily molded; and when it dries, it becomes very hard. Most clay contains a mineral called kaolinite, which consists of aluminum combined with other elements. In New Jersey, much of the clay contains iron. When the clay is baked, the iron causes the product to have a red color. This makes most Jersey clay unsuitable for fine china. Most of the clay used

197

in making china and porcelain is now imported from the southern part of the United States or from England. This clay does not contain iron.

There are thick beds of clay in Mercer, Middlesex, and Monmouth Counties. The largest clay pit in New Jersey is near Sayreville, in Middlesex County. Clay has been mined here for over one hundred years. Clay mining is one of our oldest industries. Bricks were made at Trenton at the time of the Revolutionary War. New Jersey clay is still used to make tiles, terra cotta, flowerpots, bricks, and fire-bricks. This clay comes chiefly from clay pits located at Parlin, Cheesequake, South Amboy, Sayreville, and Woodbridge.

Sand

In the southern part of New Jersey, in Camden, Cumberland, and Ocean Counties, sand is a very valuable resource. Some of the sand, which is a very pure grade of quartz sand, is used in glass-making. One factory in Bridgeton makes one million glass bottles daily. Other sand is well suited for use as a moulding sand and is used in foundry work. This type of sand is found in Burlington, Cumberland, Middlesex, and Monmouth Counties.

At Cape May Point, in Cape May County, the sand is of a particularly fine grade for use as a water filter. The sand is composed of grains which are round in shape. Round grains do not pack as tightly as do grains which are angular in shape. If the grains pack too tightly, the water will not filter through the sand as rapidly as it should. Cape May sand is shipped to many parts of the United States to be used for water filtering. Some has even been shipped to Europe, for use in filtration plants there.

Still a different type of sand is found at Old Bridge, in

Middlesex County. This sand has grains of very uniform size and is used in making asphalt.

Sand is also used for manufacturing scouring soaps and metal polishes.

Sand is formed by the decay of hard rocks, such as granite. The softer minerals have disappeared, leaving the hard sand grains.

Greensand Marl

New Jersey is the only state in the union which produces greensand marl in commercial quantities. This substance is found on the Coastal Plain, in Burlington, Camden, Gloucester, Monmouth, and Salem Counties. As the name indicates, it looks like green sand. The marl is found in beds 20 to 25 feet thick. These beds reach the surface between Delaware Bay and Atlantic Highlands, near Sandy Hook. Greensand marl is rich in potassium, nitrogen, and iron, and was formed by the decay of sediments containing shells of tiny sea animals Farmers formerly used it as a fertilizer. Some farmers in the area still use it for this purpose. After proper preparation, greensand marl makes an excellent water-softening compound. It removes the calcium and other minerals which are in some hard water. These objectionable minerals clog pipes and waste soap. Several companies sell water softeners which contain greensand marl.

In some of the marl beds, fossil remains of turtles, clamshells, and crocodiles have been found. These creatures lived in New Jersey millions of years ago. Where the marl beds now are was once a sea.

Some day, these marl beds may be used as a source of potash. Today it is cheaper to obtain potash from other sources.

199

Peat

Peat is one of New Jersey's least-known natural resources. It is found in many swamps in southern New Jersey and in the swamps and remains of glacial lakes in northern New Jersey. There are large deposits of peat in Bergen, Morris, Sussex, and Warren Counties. Here plant materials died and decayed for centuries, forming deposits of peat which are several feet thick. Some of these deposits cover many acres. New Jersey peat is not burned for fuel, as peat is in some European countries. In New Jersey, peat is sold to florists and gardeners, who use it to supply organic matter to the soil. It is very good for holding moisture in garden soils. Poultry raisers also use peat as a litter on the floor of chicken houses. After it absorbs the droppings of the chickens, it is put out on the soil, making good fertilizer.

The most important use of peat is for gardening purposes. It is used to make some chemical fertilizer mixtures which are sold as a substitute for manure.

Limestone

Limestone is a rock which was formed under the ocean or an inland sea. The lime from which the rock was formed came from one of two sources. One source was older rocks which were dissolved by water. When the water had more dissolved lime than it could hold, the lime was deposited by the water on the ocean bottom. The second source of the lime was the remains of sea animals, like oysters, clams, and scallops. When these animals died, their shells were ground up by the water into very small particles. These small particles became cemented together to form limestone.

Limestone is found in many parts of northern Jersey. Hunterdon, Warren, and Sussex Counties have large deposits. At one time, the limestone was used to make cement. It was quarried for this purpose at Franklin in Sussex County, and near New Village, Stewardsville, and Alpha in Warren County. Cement is an important product made from limestone by grinding the limestone with shale, clay, and other substances. Cement is used to make sidewalks, roads, and buildings.

At Clinton in Warren County, Newton in Sussex County, and Peapack in Somerset County, limestone is at present quarried and heated to produce lime. Limestone crumbles into a powder when it is heated. The limestone changes to lime and carbon dioxide as a result of the heating process. The carbon dioxide is given off as a gas. Lime is used to make plaster and mortar, and in the manufacture of many articles such as paper, glass, and bleaching powders. Lime is also used by farmers and gardeners to sweeten the soil or, in other words, to make the soil less acid.

Traprock

Traprock is a rock which is very important commercially. Traprock was formed in an interesting manner. Many thousands of years ago, large quantities of hot liquid rock, rising from deep in the earth, flowed out through cracks in the solid rock, onto the earth's surface. This was what is called a lava flow. Later, the lava cooled and formed a very hard rock. At other places, the hot liquid rock squeezed its way in between layers of rock near the earth's surface. Here, when it could, it formed thick sheets of hard rock. Later, these sheets of hard rock were uncovered by erosion, which wore away the layers above. Both these dark-colored, hard rocks are called "traprock" by building contractors. Geologists call the type which cooled at the surface of the earth "basalt." The type that cooled as thick layers or sheets under the earth's surface is called "diabase." Diabase has larger crystals than basalt.

Traprock is found throughout the Appalachian Province in the section called the Piedmont Plain. It is quarried in large quantities in Mercer, Passaic, and Somerset Counties. Smaller quarries are found in other counties.

The Palisades, which we shall learn more about in the next section of this chapter, are composed of diabase. The Watchung and Orange Mountains are composed of basalt.

There is nothing better than traprock for making roads and railroad beds. The rock is crushed into small pieces for these purposes. Huge blocks of this rock are taken to the seashore, where they are dumped into the ocean to make jetties. The jetties help prevent erosion of the beaches by the waves and currents.

Traprock is used in some places to make concrete. Because of its hardness and poor color it is not used as a building stone. New Jersey leads all the other states in the production of traprock.

Sandstone

Sandstone is a rock made from grains of sand that have been cemented together naturally. The cementing agent is usually either lime or iron. There are quarries at Raven Rock and at Stockton in Hunterdon County which produce sandstone of a high grade. The stone is cut into blocks suitable for building purposes. When this is done, the stone is said to be "dressed." The dressed stone is used in the construction of fine buildings. Many beautiful homes were once built in New York City and in Philadelphia from sandstone quarried in New Jersey. Today, although there is still an abundance of sandstone, only two quarries produce it. It is too expensive to quarry and to use.

Granite

Granite is a very hard and durable rock. It is one of the rocks formed by the solidification of liquid rock deep in the earth. This type of rock is called an igneous rock. Granite is usually light-colored, but the color varies, depending upon the mineral content. Granite is used to make buildings, tombstones, and monuments.

New Jersey has lots of granite which could be used for the above purposes, but today dressed granite is not produced in the state. There is a considerable production of crushed stone of granitic type. This is used for making roads.

Argillite

This is a close-grained, hard, mud rock, occurring in a variety of colors. Not so long ago, there were quarries producing this rock at Princeton and Lawrenceville in Mercer County. Many of the buildings on the campus of Princeton University were built of this stone. These quarries are not operating at present, although they may renew operation at some future date. There is an abundance of argillite, but labor costs are too high to quarry and build with it.

Shale

Shale is formed from mud which hardens under pressure. It is very abundant, particularly in central New Jersey, but it has small commercial value. Shale does not make a good building stone, because it weathers easily. In some parts of the state, shale is used for road construction. It is not well suited for this, because shale breaks down into mud when it is wet and under pressure. At Port Murray, in Warren County, and in some parts of Bergen County, shale is mixed with glacial drift and made into bricks. Glacial drift is fine earth once carried by ice masses which came into our state from the North.

Slate

There are large quantities of slate in New Jersey, but the quarrying of it has been abandoned. The Pennsylvania slate, which is part of the same beds, is a little better in quality. The demand for New Jersey slate has decreased so that it is not profitable to produce it commercially. Slate is a rock formed from mud and hardened by tremendous pressure and heat. It splits into thin sheets and is therefore useful for such things as shingles and blackboards.

Oil

Oil is found in sand, and because there is sand in New Jersey, many people believe that there should also be oil. However, New Jersey does not have any known oil-bearing sands. According to our state geologist, the probabilities of ever finding any oil in the state are very slight.

Many wells have been drilled in New Jersey by people seeking oil. Some have gone almost one mile deep. All of them were failures and have been abandoned.

Coal

It is very improbable that coal will ever be discovered in our state. Conditions in ancient times were never right for its formation.

Uranium Ores

Some people believe that valuable uranium ores may be found in the state. Our state geologist, who has made a careful study of the subject, does not believe that large commercial deposits of uranium ores will ever be found here. Perhaps some small workable deposits may be found in the northern part of the state. Specimens of good uranium were first found in 1954.

Magnesia

At Cape May Point, in Cape May County, there is a recent development which is of interest. Here a mineral product called magnesia is being extracted from the ocean. Magnesia is another name for magnesium oxide, from which the metal magnesium is produced. Large quantities of ocean water are brought into the processing plant of the Northwest Magnesite Company, where the magnesia is extracted. In 1953, about 2,760 tons of pure magnesia were produced.

Magnesium, the metal made from the magnesia or magnesium oxide, is a light, strong metal, very much in demand in industry. It weighs only two thirds as much as aluminum and is used with aluminum to make alloys. These alloys are very light and strong metals, used to make aircraft frames, pistons, and other lightweight appliances. Magnesium is also used in flash bulbs and in signal flares.

CONCLUSION

We have seen in this section of the chapter that New Jersey does have a number of valuable rocks and minerals. Several thousand people earn their living by working in industries which bring this "buried treasure" to the surface.

New Jersey will never rank as high in the value of its rocks and minerals as many of the other states. Other states have natural fuels, like oil and coal, which make them rank higher. However, it is possible that new uses will be found for our rocks and minerals. Scientists are always looking for new uses for natural resources. Perhaps some day you will make a contribution in this big field.

Section 3. SOME SCENIC FEATURES OF NEW JERSEY

Perhaps it seems strange to you to include a section on scenery in this chapter. Possibly you never thought of scenery as a natural resource. In Chapter One, it was said that natural resources were things which were given to us by nature and which were of benefit and value to man. Certainly, beautiful scenery is a natural resource under this definition. Most of our scenery is based on the kind of rocks that are in the earth, as a person's face is based on its bones. Natural forces acting on these rocks over long periods of time have made them as they are. That is why a description of a few of the most important scenic features of New Jersey has been included in this chapter.

There is scenery of sufficient variety in this state to please nearly everyone. Some people like the mountains and others prefer the seashore. Some see beauty when the sun rises or sets over a lake or a marsh. Although New Jersey is a small state, it offers a great variety of scenery.

We learned in Chapter One that New Jersey is made up of four quite distinct sections or zones, marked off by lines that run almost northeast to southwest. Let us now look at some of the state's scenic features, starting with the zone or section that is farthest north.

Kittatinny Mountain

In the northwestern section of the state is a beautiful range of high hills called Kittatinny Mountain. In Pennsylvania, the extension of this ridge is the Blue Mountain. This long mountain is composed of a very hard rock called quartzite. Quartzite is not the same as quartz. Quartz is a mineral. Quartzite is a rock composed of quartz and other minerals. Quartzite has been hardened by heat and pressure. Because of its hardness, it is not easily eroded or worn away. The top of Kittatinny Mountain is quite narrow and remarkably level. Once it was part of a large plain that existed in this part of the country. The softer rocks surrounding the quartzite were eroded, leaving the mountain. Along the top of the ridge runs the Appalachian Trail, which extends from Maine to Georgia. This is the longest foot trail in the United States. Those who hike along it enjoy beautiful views, and the New Jersey section is particularly scenic. It is well worth seeing. The state has erected a shelter at Sun Rise Mountain. This can be reached by automobiles. It is possible to look out from this spot for many miles over the Kittatinny Valley, which lies between Kittatinny Mountain and the Highlands. The valley contains many rich and well-kept farms.

Delaware Water Gap

Where the Delaware River cuts through Kittatinny Mountain, there is a place called the Delaware Water Gap. For several millions of years, the Delaware River has been eroding or cutting into the hard rock of the mountain. Many years ago, strong forces within the earth caused parts of the land to rise. At the same time, the river was cutting down to make its channel. This is similar to a moving saw being held at one level, while a thick plank is slowly raised under the saw. The water represents the saw, and the earth is the plank. A V-shaped cut was made, due to the slow erosion of the stream. The rocks along the river above and below the Water Gap are softer than those right at the Gap. They have, therefore, been more easily worn away by the river. That is why the stream was able to widen its valley so much above and below the Water Gap. At the Water Gap, rain, frost, and temperature changes have loosened great blocks of quartzite. These have fallen down the mountainside. As the larger

Courtesy of N. J. State Museum

Delaware Water Gap looking south from New Jersey

pieces are broken still smaller, they are carried away by the river. The sides of the Delaware Water Gap rise abruptly 1,200 feet above the river. The distance across the Gap at the top is less than one mile. People come from all over the eastern part of the United States to drive through the Gap.

Waterfalls

Because of the hardness of the rocks in the Appalachian Province, there are a number of waterfalls of great beauty in the northern part of the state. These waterfalls have been produced by several different sets of conditions.

N. J. Dept. of Conservation
and Economic Development

Buttermilk Falls in Sussex County

One cause of waterfalls is that streams often have in their beds rocks of different degrees of hardness. The softer rock of the stream bed wears away faster than the hard rock, leaving the hard rock standing at a greater height. This is one cause of a waterfall. Also, the stream may have rocks in its bed which have cracks or "joints" in them. The water eats away the sides of such a joint till there is a waterfall. Several waterfalls in Sussex County were formed because of these conditions.

Two lovely little waterfalls are located at Tillman's Ravine and at Cooper's Glen in Sussex County. One of these, Buttermilk Falls, has a vertical drop of 200 feet. It tumbles over a series of moss-covered steps.

At Paterson, on the Passaic River, there is a ridge of traprock which cuts directly across the stream. Traprock is very hard and resists the erosion of the stream. The softer rock downstream has been cut away. When the river is full, this waterfall is very beautiful. It is only 70 feet high, but it is quite wide. As we learned earlier, Paterson was located where it is because in the early days of our country, the waterfall was used for power. Today, the waterfall is used to generate electricity. For this purpose, much of the water is diverted from the falls, so the waterfall is seldom seen at its best.

Palisades

An outstanding feature of the Piedmont Plain is the Palisades. The Palisades are a wall of rock rising 500 feet above the Hudson River. Over 150 million years ago, hot, liquid rock was squeezed out from deep in the earth. It was forced in between layers of shale and sandstone. You might think of the layers of shale and sandstone as pieces of bread in a sandwich. The liquid rock represents the filling put between the slices of bread. After many years, the hot, liquid rock cooled and became solid, forming a hard layer. Geologists call a layer like this a "sill." Later, the surface was worn away by water and other eroding agents. This was like the top

The Palisades

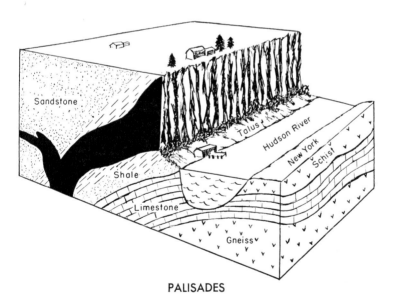

Sandstone

Shale

Limestone

Talus

Hudson River

New York

Schist

Gneiss

PALISADES

being eaten off the sandwich. The remainder of the sandwich was tilted by strong forces in the earth, so that the remains of the sill dip down under New Jersey. Later the Hudson River cut down through the sandwich, so that the edge of the sill is exposed. Geologists come from all over the world to study the Palisades.

Watchung and Orange Mountains

The Watchung and Orange Mountains were formed at about the same time as the Palisades, over 150 million years ago. Where these mountains are, hot, liquid rock came up out of cracks and flowed over the surface of the earth. After this liquid rock cooled, mud was deposited on it by streams that flowed over the rock. This mud hardened to form shale. The process of hot, liquid rock spilling out and cooling was repeated several times. After each time, more mud hardened on it. Thousands of years later, powerful forces, deep in the earth, tilted sections of this rock. Some parts were raised higher than others. Geologists call this movement of land in which some sections are raised higher than others nearby "faulting." Tilting and faulting, along with stream erosion, were the chief causes of these hills. After the land was raised, water cut down through the softer shale, making valleys. The several ridges of the Watchung and Orange Mountains were formed by the hard igneous rock resisting the erosion that cut out the valleys. We call these ridges "mountains" but they are really only hills. Many fine residential areas have been built here.

Beaches

To many people, our white sand beaches are the most attractive part of the state. These beaches extend from Sandy Hook on the north to Cape May Point on the south. Every year, millions of people are attracted to them. Some people come from great distances to enjoy the beautiful beaches of our state. Some sections of the beach have plants and animals that are not found anywhere else along the eastern coast of

Lewis D. Crowell

Sand dunes at Island Beach

our country. Island Beach is one such area. This was purchased by the state in 1954, so that it might be enjoyed by the public. It will be a state park soon. Perhaps some of it will be used as a bathing beach. It is the hope of many people, however, that a large part of this beach will be left in its natural state, as a sort of natural museum. It would be a great pity to destroy the beauty of such a rare beach.

Beaches were formed by the depositing of sand from

streams and rivers. These streams and rivers brought the sand from the higher lands to the west of the present beaches and deposited it under the water which once covered the area.

Much of the sand has been tossed up by waves into sand bars. A sand bar is a narrow ridge of sand, up to a half mile in width, running along the coast. There is usually water on both sides of the sand bar. On one side of our sand bar beaches, we have the Atlantic Ocean. On the other side are bays or, as they are sometimes called, "lagoons." Atlantic City and many of our summer resorts are built on sand bars of the sort described. Perhaps you can locate on a map other towns or cities built upon sand bars. Sometimes these large bars are called "barrier beaches." This name is used when the bar is wide and extends a long way.

At the northern end of our beaches, the barrier beach ends in a hook, formed of sand deposited there by ocean currents. It is called, very appropriately, "Sandy Hook." The United States government now uses Sandy Hook as a part of our defense system. Some day, it may become a state park.

Along part of the coast, wind has rolled grains of sand into "dunes." The dunes eventually become covered with plant life and are very attractive features of the coast.

Tidal Marshes

In many places, there are salt-water marshes back of the barrier beaches. Some day, these will be filled in by the moving sand. Now, however, they afford splendid homes for wildlife. Muskrats and other animals abound there. Many thousands of acres of this marshland have been bought by the Division of Fish and Game and are being developed as Public Hunting and Fishing Grounds. The marshes have a beauty all their own.

Lakes

Lakes are very numerous in New Jersey and add much to the beauty of the state. Beside many of the lakes, there are well-known summer resorts. Lake Hopatcong, for example, is known to many persons from outside New Jersey. Other lakes are less well known, even to residents of the state. The lakes of New Jersey were formed in different ways.

About 70 of our lakes were formed, either directly or indirectly, by glacial ice sheets. These glacial ice sheets, as you know, were huge, thick masses of ice that invaded our state from the North thousands of years ago. The ice sheets carried in them and on them many stones and much dirt. These materials were dumped by the ice when it melted. Where the glacier ended, the material it deposited is called a "terminal moraine." In New Jersey, the last ice sheet left a terminal moraine which forms a series of low hills. The hills extend across the state near Belvidere, Hackettstown, and Morristown. Some of these stones and masses of dirt blocked the old stream beds that were already cut in the land. Behind these deposits, the water was dammed up, and lakes were formed. Even though 7,000 years or more have passed since the last glaciation in this state, the lakes still exist. Some of the lakes formed in the manner just described are Lake Hopatcong, Green Pond, Budd Lake, and Lake Mashipacong. Can you find these on a map of New Jersey? They are all in the northwestern part of the state.

Other lakes are thought to have been formed by huge blocks of ice which were left behind after the glacier had receded to the North. When the blocks of ice broke off from the main ice sheet, sand and mud were deposited all around them. Later, the ice melted slowly, and huge hollows were

215

left in the sand and mud where the ice had been. Some lakes formed in this manner are Franklin Lake in Bergen County and Lost Lake in Sussex County.

In southern Jersey, there are also many lakes. These were formed in other ways, since the ice sheet did not go onto what is now the Coastal Plain. Some of the lakes here were formed by the damming up of stream beds by sediments deposited by the stream. The lake formed behind the dam. Some of the lakes in our state are man-made. Man either dredged out swamps and low land or built dams across the streams.

The Plains

In Burlington and Ocean Counties there are about 15,000 acres of sandy soil which are covered with low, scrubby pine, oak, and laurel. In the spring, this area is quite beautiful. The plants remain small and stunted because of repeated forest fires over many years. Most of the trees grow only five or six feet tall. Some people think that the soil is different here and lacks minerals needed by plants. Studies have shown, however, that the real cause is repeated burnings of the land.

CONCLUSION

The above are a few points of interest that you may want to visit some day. Perhaps your parents will take you on a trip, so that you can see and possibly photograph these and other interesting places in our state. As you get further advanced in school, you may want to learn more about the ways nature has formed these scenic features. The study of such things is a part of the science of geology. While you are traveling around the state, you may want to start a mineral or a rock collection. This can become a hobby that will interest you long after you leave school.

SOME THINGS TO THINK ABOUT

1. Why is shale not used as a building stone, even though it is very abundant in New Jersey?

2. Why are minerals said to be non-renewable resources?

3. Why are fewer homes being made of stone than were made fifty years ago?

4. Once many farmers used local deposits of limestone to make lime for their soil. Why is this not done so much at present?

5. How does the geologist distinguish between a rock and a mineral?

6. Why are most of the minerals with commercial value found in the northern part of the state?

7. The Palisades and the Watchung Mountains are both made of traprock. The rock in the Palisades has larger crystals than the rock in the Watchung Mountain. Can you figure out why this might be? Think of where they were formed with reference to the earth's surface.

8. What cities or towns do you know of that were settled originally because of the presence of waterfalls or water power?

9. What towns or cities were originally settled because of some rock or mineral resource that was in the area?

10. If a stream carries rocks, sand, and fine mud, which of these will be deposited first when that stream enters a lake or other large body of water? Why?

SOME THINGS TO DO

1. Examine some rocks, noting the presence of crystals, color differences, and hardness.

2. Dissolve a tablespoonful of salt, borax, or alum in a glass of water. Set the glass in a warm place, and when the water

217

has evaporated, examine the crystals that have formed on the side of the glass.

3. Make a collection of some common rocks and minerals.

4. Read in a science book about igneous, sedimentary, and metamorphic rocks. Classify the ones mentioned in the text.

5. Find out from a building contractor what rocks are used to build homes in your vicinity.

6. Visit a museum in a large city, and observe the collection of rocks and minerals which you find there.

7. Dissolve a piece of chalk in a few tablespoonfuls of vinegar, to see how minerals go into solution.

8. Make models out of clay or sand to show some of the scenic features mentioned in the text. Such models might show barrier beaches, hooks, mountains, and waterfalls.

9. Take a trip to see some of the scenic features mentioned in this chapter.

10. Take photographs of some interesting scenic features.

11. Mark on a map of the state one place where each of the rocks and minerals mentioned in the text is found.

12. Examine some sand with a hand lens to see if it is round or angular.

13. Look up in a science book the information on how cement is made from limestone and how it is used.

14. Write a story about the history of the iron industry in New Jersey, referring to an encyclopedia or history for information.

SOME TERMS YOU NEED TO KNOW

Dunes—Heaps of sand blown by the wind.

Fossil—The preserved remains of some plant or animal.

Geologist—A scientist who studies the materials in the earth and the forces producing changes in the earth.

Glacial drift—Any of the materials carried by an ice sheet or glacier.

Ice sheet—A thick mass of ice, covering a large section of the country.

Joints—Cracks in the solid rocks of the earth.

Lava—Hot, liquid rock, which flows over the surface of the earth.

Marsh—An area of soft, wet land.

Non-renewable resources—Natural resources, such as minerals, which cannot be replaced for millions of years.

Ore—A natural substance containing one or more metals.

Renewable resources—Natural resources which can be replaced over long periods of time. Forests and animal life are examples.

Traprock—A name used to describe rocks formed where hot, liquid rock has solidified at or near the surface. Used in New Jersey to describe diabase or basalt.

Chapter Nine

The Air Around Us

Section 1. THE NATURE AND IMPORTANCE OF AIR

Pure air is a very important natural resource. Because it is so common, many people do not think of it as a natural resource. Not one of us could live more than a few minutes without pure air to breathe. We take into our bodies each day more air, by weight, than we do food or water. For thousands of years, the air that man breathed was quite pure. Then came a time when the air grew much less pure than it used to be. This is particularly true of the air in the large cities where so many of us live. In cities, much of the air is badly polluted. It usually has in it gases and particles of dirt and soot. Many of these substances are objectionable to humans and in some cases, they are harmful to plant and animal life. Some affect our property, by destroying paint, for example. Getting pure air for our cities may cost as much as getting pure, clean water.

Scientists at Rutgers University have made tests to find out how much soot and dust occur in air in New Jersey. They found that in suburban areas almost three ounces of soot and dust fall every day on a piece of land measuring 50 feet by 100 feet. In a city lot of the same size, the amount is even more. In cities with many industries, about one pound of soot and dust falls every day on a lot 50 feet by 100 feet.

Think of how much material falls on an entire city during a year!

Air should be used wisely, just as should the soils of our state and the water supply. This chapter will tell us a little about the air around us. We shall also learn about some of

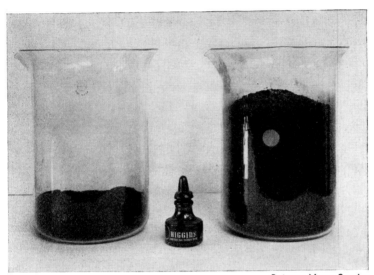

Rutgers News Service

Average daily amount of soot that falls on a 50-by-100 foot lot in heavily industrialized area of New Jersey (one pound) compared with amount that falls in suburban area (.17 pounds)

the problems of keeping air clean. We shall see that there are several things that all of us can do to improve the quality of the air which we breathe.

First, let us find out what air is. Most of us know that it is a real substance, even though we cannot see clean, pure air. We have felt air when the wind has blown on our faces. Wind is simply air in motion. We have all heard sounds that have been caused by moving air. When wind whistles through the trees or telephone wires, sounds are being made by air.

221

All sounds are caused by waves of air striking our eardrums. We have all seen how a basketball or a football fills with air when we pump or blow air into it. These things should prove to us that air is a real substance.

The earth is entirely surrounded with a thick layer of air. This air, or atmosphere, as it is called, extends hundreds of miles above the earth's surface. The atmosphere is composed of a mixture of many gases. There are several gases that are quite abundant in air and many others that occur only in traces. Studies made with rockets show that the air 100 miles above the earth's surface is chemically the same as air near the surface, except for impurities that man has added to the air near the earth's surface. Because of air currents and winds, the atmosphere is well mixed, so that it all has the same composition.

The gas most abundant in the atmosphere is nitrogen. Nitrogen is a colorless gas, which makes up about 78 per cent of pure, dry air. Nitrogen is an important part of organic materials. Green plants need lots of nitrogen, but they cannot use the atmospheric nitrogen directly. Most nitrogen used by plants comes from fertilizers or decayed plant and animal materials. Some bacteria can take nitrogen from the air and put it into the soil. Green plants then take it from the soil and build it into their bodies.

Approximately 20 per cent of pure, dry air is oxygen. Oxygen is what the chemists call an active gas. It combines easily with many other substances. Oxygen is necessary for breathing for all plants and animals. Human beings take oxygen into their bodies through either the nose or the mouth. The nose has hairs in it which strain or filter out some of the dust particles that may be in air. The nose also warms the air before it reaches the lungs. It is better, therefore, to breathe through the nose. In our lungs, the oxygen is separated from the other gases of the air and enters the blood stream, which carries it to all parts of the body. The oxygen combines with food to produce energy. This is what keeps us warm and enables us to move around and carry on our daily activities.

Carbon dioxide is another very important gas found in the air. Only 0.03 per cent of the air is normally carbon dioxide, but this small amount is very necessary for plant life. Without carbon dioxide, plants could not manufacture food. Without plant food, animals and human beings could not live long. In your science classes, you will learn more about photosynthesis, which is the name of the important process by which plants use carbon dioxide and water to make foods.

Ozone is another gas which occurs in the air in small quantities. It is important to us because it stops those rays of the sun which cause sunburn from reaching the earth in large amounts. Were the ozone to disappear from the atmosphere, we could not live. The ultraviolet rays which cause sunburn would kill us. On the other hand, if too much ozone were in the air, we would not receive enough of the ultraviolet rays, and then vitamin D would not be produced in our bodies. Without vitamin D, our bones would not develop properly. Thus we see that ozone is an important part of the air.

There are small quantities of other gases in the air. Some of these are: neon, xenon, helium, and hydrogen. Most of these are not very important to us, although scientists have found uses for some. Of course, air usually has water vapor in it. This water vapor is very beneficial to us. Without it, our bodies, both inside and outside, would become too dry and parched.

Most of the air which we breathe has dust and other impurities in it. They pollute the air so that it is harmful to man. Polluted air often causes eyes to smart. It frequently irritates the throat. Not only may it cause severe illness, but sometimes

223

it causes death. Polluted air also damages property, as we shall see.

Section 2. THE POLLUTION OF AIR

There are many ways in which air becomes polluted. In some cases, we cannot do much to prevent pollution. If, however, the public works together with the health officers, something can be done about most pollution problems. Let us look at some of the ways in which air becomes polluted.

Pollen

Pollen is the name given to the very small particles of material produced in the flowers of plants. Pollen is often blown by the wind so that it floats in the air far away from the plant which produced it. Some people are very sensitive to certain kinds of pollen in the air. The pollen makes their eyes water, and they act as though they had a severe cold. Some pollen produces an illness called hay fever in these people. The pollen from some plants, such as ragweed, is particularly objectionable in causing hay fever and other ailments of the respiratory system. We should all learn to recognize ragweed and encourage property owners to destroy it in the summer, before the pollen is produced. If this is done, air pollution will be lessened.

Dust and Smoke

Dust and smoke both pollute the air and may affect our comfort and health. By keeping the soil covered with grass and other cover crops, dust can be reduced. We have already seen that this will prevent soil erosion. Paving city and town streets will also eliminate much dust. We should not burn leaves, trash, or paper in such a way as to cause smoke. It is better not to burn these things at all. Leaves, particularly, make good soil when they are rotted, and they should be saved for this purpose. If it is absolutely necessary to burn these, or other things, it should be done in such a manner as not to make too much smoke. Apartment houses often burn waste matter in incinerators. If this is done, adequate precautions should be taken so that smoke does not get into the air in large quantities.

Automobile Exhausts

In cities, one very common form of pollution is caused by automobiles. You have all seen, I am sure, the smoke that sometimes comes from the exhausts of cars. This is often quite black. It usually means that the car is not being operated properly or is in need of repair. A car owner should have his car checked by a mechanic if it smokes very much. This smoking not only wastes oil, but it pollutes the air which others breathe.

Even when a car is in good condition, the burning gasoline causes some soot and gases to be discharged into the air. One of these gases is carbon monoxide. This is not the same as carbon dioxide, which was discussed earlier. Carbon monoxide can cause death, if breathed in very small quantities. Breathing a very little amount of carbon monoxide causes one to become drowsy and sleepy. This may make a driver of an automobile become careless and result in an accident.

When riding in a car, we should be sure to have a little fresh air at all times. Carbon monoxide may enter through the ventilating system of the car, when it is driven close behind another car in heavy traffic. Many inventors are working on devices to collect or destroy the soot and gases in automobile exhausts.

225

Automobile exhaust fumes form ozone when exposed to sunlight. Ozone is a gas which irritates the nose and throat.

Automobile Tires

Automobile tires also add dust to the air. In its lifetime, one tire produces, by friction with the road surface, 750 billion rubber particles. Most of these enter the air and pollute it. Careful driving can reduce this pollution somewhat.

Industrial Pollution of the Air

Much of the air pollution in New Jersey comes from industries which send objectionable gases into the air from their smokestacks and chimneys. You will remember that New

Standard Oil Co. (N. J.)

New Jersey's industries are one source of air pollution.

Jersey has many oil refineries, chemical works, and other industries. Not only are the odors from some of these industries annoying, but many of the impurities they give off may affect our health. These impurities also injure or kill trees and sometimes even affect the paint on bridges and on buildings in large cities. Some of the bridges in the industrial areas of the state have to be painted often, because of damage done by chemicals in the air.

Smog

Most of us have read in the papers or heard on radio or television about smog. "Smog" is a word which originally meant a combination of smoke and fog. Now it is used to describe any weather condition that produces irritation in our breathing organs. Much illness has been caused by smog, and many people have died from it. California and Pennsylvania in our country and London, England, have all had serious cases of smog in recent years. New Jersey has not had any serious smog. Smog is caused by weather conditions which prevent the movement of the air for several days. Poisonous gases remain at, or near, the surface of the earth. In New Jersey, the land is flat in those places where the air might contain poisonous gases. Where land is flat, the air does not usually remain in one place very long. The gases blow away. The poisonous gases that help make the smog are usually produced in factories or industrial plants.

Atomic Explosions

Unlimited testing of the H- and A-bombs by nations all over the world may pollute the air. The products of atomic explosions may give off harmful radiations for thousands of years. Some scientists believe that this will become dangerous.

227

Perhaps some day the nations of the world will agree to restrict the use of atomic bombs. It would help now if all nations would agree to limit the number of test explosions made in any one year.

Section 3. THE PREVENTION OF AIR POLLUTION

It has already been shown that the individual can do much to prevent pollution of the air. He can be careful about producing smoke. He can drive cars that are in good condition mechanically. He can apply brakes carefully, so that dust from the tires will not fly into the air. He can also control the growth of plants, such as ragweed, which are to blame for objectionable pollen in the air.

Industries can do much to prevent air pollution, also. Many factories are taking steps to prevent pollution of the air by the products which go up their chimneys. One way they control this is by building higher chimneys or smokestacks. The gases are then sent higher into the air and are more widely scattered. No one place gets so many of the impurities.

A better method to prevent pollution of the air by a factory is to put devices into the chimney to cause the dust and other impurities to settle out of the air before leaving the chimney. There are other devices which can be put into the chimney to cause the gases to be completely burned without making smoke.

If all the people of our state insist on having pure air to breathe, industries will cooperate in preventing pollution of the air. If the public is not interested, progress will not come so rapidly. This, then, is another way individuals can be of help in preventing air pollution.

Powerhouses, trains, open dump fires, and home heating

Esso Standard Oil Co.

Air pollution before the introduction of the smokeless flare

Esso Standard Oil Co.

Air pollution reduced by the introduction of the smokeless flare

systems all contribute impurities to the air. These, too, can be controlled if enough people became interested. An educated and interested public can usually bring about needed changes in our state.

The State Department of Health

The New Jersey State Department of Health has been doing all it can to help keep the air of our state clean. In

N. J. State Dept. of Health

Interior of Mobile Laboratory showing industrial hygiene engineer doing "on the spot" tests

1954, the state legislature passed a law to help the Department in its efforts. This law is one of the first of its kind in the nation. It will bring together in a commission many experienced persons. They will study methods of air pollution control and make rules and regulations for industries and cities to follow.

This commission is under the State Department of Health. The Department will continue, in addition to commission activities, its program of research and investigation to im-

N. J. State Dept. of Health

Mobile Air Pollution Laboratory

prove the air of our state. This work is carried on by the Bureau of Adult and Occupational Health.

The Bureau of Adult and Occupational Health has designed what is called a Mobile Air Pollution Laboratory. This is a large trailer, drawn by an automobile. The trailer is equipped with many kinds of apparatus for studying the air. It is really a small chemical laboratory on wheels. Whenever a report is received about air pollution, the laboratory is taken to the place involved. Samples of air are examined. After several days of study, the engineers with the laboratory

231

can discover what caused the pollution of the air. They can also find out what factory probably was responsible for putting the objectionable substances in the air. The engineers can make recommendations to the owners of the factory, as to how to eliminate the impurities.

CONCLUSIONS

It is estimated that in the United States, air pollution costs five million dollars a year. These costs are for damages done

Esso Standard Oil Co.

Charting air pollution. Scale models help scientists to determine factors that will eliminate or reduce pollution.

to property by gases in the air. In addition, air pollution affects both our comfort and our health.

Every individual should do all that he can to prevent air pollution. The conservation of property and human health and life is important. If you are doing all that you can to prevent air pollution, you are making a contribution to better living.

If the air in your community is polluted and objectionable, your local health officer should be notified. If he needs help, he will call on the State Department of Health. Many parts of the state, particularly in the industrial areas, could be made better places in which to live if the air were purer.

SOME THINGS TO THINK ABOUT

1. Why is the air in New Jersey more impure now than it was one hundred years ago?

2. Why is it better to breathe through the nose than through the mouth?

3. Why is the oxygen of the air so important to us?

4. What are some of the things that individuals can do to prevent air pollution?

5. Why should one not rely entirely on the ventilation system found in many of the newer cars when one is driving in heavy traffic?

6. What sources of air pollution are there near your home or school?

SOME THINGS TO DO

1. Find out from a science book or other source what diseases may be caused by air which is polluted.

2. Find out from the janitor in your school what makes fires smoke and how he prevents it.

3. Ask a service station attendant or garage mechanic to save an old exhaust pipe from a car, so that you can see how it is constructed and how it works.

4. Look around your neighborhood and see if you can find any ragweed which you may be able to destroy.

5. Collect newspaper items about smog and air pollution, and show them to your class.

6. Look at chimneys in your neighborhood and see if any are smoking excessively.

7. See if you can detect any objectionable odors in your community and, if so, find out where they come from.

8. Talk with your parents and other members of the community about air pollution, so that they will become aware of the problem.

9. Look at ragweed pollen under a compound microscope, if one is available.

SOME TERMS YOU NEED TO KNOW

Breathing—The process by which air is taken into the body and waste products are given off.

Pollen—Very small particles produced on the flowers of plants to aid in the reproductive process.

Respiratory system—The organs of the body which are used in breathing.

Smog—Any weather condition which produces irritation of our respiratory system.

Useful Source Books

Here is a list of the references principally used in writing this book. Much information, often basic, was acquired by interviews with specialists in the field of conservation in the state of New Jersey. Readers will find the volumes listed below useful for more detailed treatment of many topics.

Annual Report, 1954, Division of Fish and Game. Trenton, New Jersey Department of Conservation and Economic Development, 1954.

Breder, Charles M., *Field Book of Marine Fishes of the Atlantic Coast from Labrador to Texas.* New York, G. Putnam's Sons, 1929.

Fink, Ollie E., ed., *Conservation for Tomorrow's America.* Columbus, Ohio Division of Conservation and Natural Resources in cooperation with the State Department of Education, 1942.

Fishery Resources of the United States. United States Fish and Wildlife Service. 79th Congress, first session, Senate Document 51. Washington, United States Government Printing Office, 1945.

Five Years of Pittman-Robertson Wildlife Restoration, 1949-53. Washington, Wildlife Institute, 1953.

Gabrielson, Ira M., and La Monte, Francesca R., eds., *The Fisherman's Encyclopedia.* Harrisburg, Pennsylvania, Stackpole and Heck, 1950.

Geography of New Jersey. Teacher Education Series, Curricular Syllabus 3. Trenton, New Jersey Department of Education, 1950.

Insects. United States Department of Agriculture, Yearbook, 1952. Washington, United States Government Printing Office, 1952.

Jordan, David S., and Evermann, Barton W., *American Food and Game Fishes: A Popular Account of All the Species Found in America North of the Equator, With Keys for Ready Identification, Life Histories, and Methods of Capture.* Garden City, Doubleday, Doran and Company, 1934.

Lewis, Joseph V., and Kümmel, Henry B., *The Geology of New Jersey.* New Jersey Geological Survey, Bulletin 50. Trenton, New Jersey Department of Conservation and Economic Development, 1940.

New Jersey Fish and Game Laws. Trenton, New Jersey Department of Conservation and Economic Development, 1955.

Palmer, Ephraim L., *Fieldbook of Natural History.* New York, Whittlesey House, 1949.

Parsons, Floyd W., and others, eds., *New Jersey: Life, Industries, and Resources of a Great State.* Newark, New Jersey State Chamber of Commerce, 1928.

Shoemaker, Lois M., and Morris B., *The Conservation of Native Birds.* Trenton, Department of Public Instruction, 1939.

———, *The Native Mammals of New Jersey.* Trenton, Department of Public Instruction, 1940.

Shuster, Carl N., Jr., *Observations on the Natural History of the American Horseshoe Crab.* Contribution 564. Woods Hole, Massachusetts, Woods Hole Oceanographic Institute, 1950.

Soils and Men. United States Department of Agriculture, Yearbook, 1938. Washington, United States Government Printing Office, 1938.

Trees. United States Department of Agriculture, Yearbook, 1949. Washington, United States Government Printing Office, 1949.

Warren, George C., and Burlington, H. J., comps., *The Outdoor Heritage of New Jersey.* Trenton, New Jersey Board of Fish and Game Commissioners, 1937.

Water Supply of the City of Newark, New Jersey. Newark, Department of Public Works, 1948.

Index

Air: nature and importance of, 220-223; pollution of, 220, 224-227
Agricultural Experiment Station, 77
Appalachian Mountains, 7, 8
Appalachian Province: trees of, 86-87; water in, 34; zones of, 5-8
Appalachian Valley, 5-7
Argillite, 203

Bass: food of, 164-165; sea, 171-172; species of, 164-165
Beaches, 212-214
Beavers, 138
Birds: definition of, 140; how to attract, 148-150; importance of, 140-143; kinds of, 143-147
Bluefish, 173
Bughead, see Menhaden
Butterfish, 173

Catfish, 167
Clams, 184, 188
Clay, 35-36, 197-198
Coal, 204
Coastal Plain: location of, 5, 6, 8-9, 19; rocks of, 8, 9; trees of, 90-91; wells in, 34-36

Conservation: definition of, 4, 19; of minerals, 195; of plants, 102-105; of soil, 68-75; of water, 46-51; of wildlife, 154-155
Conservation Pledge, 17-18
Contour, meaning of, 70-71
Contour planting, 76
County Agricultural Agent, 77
Crabs: blue, 180-181; horseshoe, 183-184
Crappie, 166
Crustacea, 180-183

Deer, 133-134
Delaware Water Gap, 207-208
Department of Conservation and Economic Development, 96-98, 190
Department of Health, 230-231, 233
Diversion terraces, 72-74
Division of Fish and Game, 152-154
Division of Shellfisheries, 190-191
Division of Water Policy and Supply, 51-52

Erosion: causes of, 65-66; control of, 69-75; definition of,

239

Newark Reservoir, 43
New Jersey: area of, 5; climate of, 14, 16, 19; geography of, 5-7; growing season, 15, 16; occupations in, 9, 10; population of, 3, 9

Oil, 204
Oysters, 184-188

Palisades, 210-212
Peat, 200
Perch, 166
Perch, pike, *see* Walleyed pike
Pheasant: habits of, 143-144; hunting of, 144; origin of, 143
Pickerel, chain, 168
Piedmont Plain, 7-8
Pike, walleyed, 167
Pines, 90-99
Plains, 90, 216
Pollution, *see* Air, Water
Ponds, farm, 37, 160
Porgy, 171
Precipitation: definition of, 14, 16; disposition of, 29-32
Pumpkin seed, *see* Sunfish

Quail, 145

Rabbits: damage by, 134-135; hunting of, 134; importance of, 134-135
Raccoons, 137-138
Reservoirs: definition of, 38, 56; examples of, 39-42

Resources, *see* Natural resources
Rivers: as sources of water, 39-42; of New Jersey, 9
Rocks: definition of, 194; importance of, 194; uses of, 197-204
Round Valley, 49

Sand, 34-36, 198-199
Sandstone, 202
Scallops, 189
Scup, *see* Porgy
Seines, purse, 175-177
Shad, 173-174
Shale, 203
Shrubs, 101
Slate, 204
Soil: characteristics of, 57, 60-61; classification of, 60; conservation of, 69-75; erosion of, 62-75; fertility of, 74-75; governmental agencies and, 77-79; layers of, 58-59; nature and importance of, 57
Soil Conservation Districts, 78-79
Springs, 33
Squids, 190
Squirrels, 136
State forests, 92
State parks, 92
Strip cropping, 71-72
Sunfish: food of, 165; species of, 165-166

Timber agent, 96-97
Topsoil, 58-59, 62

241